Everyday Mathematics®

The University of Chicago School Mathematics Project

Skills Link

Cumulative Practice Sets
Student Book

McGraw Hill Wright Group

The McGraw-Hill Companies

Photo Credits

Cover—Getty Images, *center*; ©Kelly Kalhoefer/Getty Images, *top right*;
©Stuart Westmorland/CORBIS, *bottom left*

Photo Collage—Herman Adler Design

www.WrightGroup.com

 **Wright Group**

Send all inquiries to:
Wright Group/McGraw-Hill
P.O. Box 812960
Chicago, IL 60681

ISBN 978-0-07-618789-8
MHID 0-07-618789-6

1 2 3 4 5 6 7 8 9 CPS 13 12 11 10 09 08 07

Contents

Practice Set 1

Write your answers below or on another piece of paper.

Write the letter of the line plot that makes sense with the survey question asked.

```
        X  X                              X
        X  X                    X         X
     X  X  X        X           X  X  X  X  X
  X  X  X  X  X  X  X      X X   X  X  X  X  X
  ─────────────────────    ──────────────────────
  0  1  2  3  4  5  6      48 50 52 54 56 58 60
```

Line Plot A   **Line Plot B**

1. How many pieces of fruit do you eat each day? _____

2. How many inches tall are you? _____

Solve.

3. 279
   + 348

4. 152
   + 67

5. 450
   − 180

6. 786
   − 239

7. 604
   − 137

8. 743
   + 865

9. 4,663
   + 2,089

10. 1,005
   − 697

11. $82 + 405 + 68 =$ _____

12. $342 - 65 =$ _____

13. $5,038 - 764 =$ _____

14. $1,456 + 79 + 382 =$ _____

Round to the nearest million.

15. 729,284,272

16. 16,839,554

_____

_____

17. 728,920

18. 1,028,265,725

_____

_____

Practice Set 1 *continued*

Write your answers below or on another piece of paper.

Use digits to write the following numbers.

19. thirty-two thousand, four hundred fifty-nine _____

20. seven hundred thousand, thirty _____

21. eight hundred thousand, six hundred nine _____

Complete each pattern. Note: There may be more than one operation per pattern set.

22. 29, 34, 39, _____, 49, _____, _____

23. 73, _____, 57, 49, 41, _____, _____

24. 45, 48, 54, 57, _____, _____, 72

25. _____, _____, 40, 33, 29, 22

26. 19, 25, 20, _____, 21, _____, _____

27. −1, _____, −3$\frac{1}{2}$, _____, −6, −7$\frac{1}{4}$, _____, _____

Complete the "What's My Rule?" tables.

28.

Rule		in	out
out = in * 310		5	1,550
		8	2,480
		11	
		15	
		18	

29.

Rule		in	out
		273	185
		330	242
			14
		246	
		510	422

Practice Set 2

Use with or after
Lesson 1·4

Write your answers below or on another piece of paper.

Find the landmarks for the following set of numbers:

9, 10, 7, 19, 12, 8, 12, 12, 8, 9, 15

1. maximum _____   **2.** minimum _____   **3.** range _____

4. median _____   **5.** mean _____   **6.** mode _____

Solve.

7. 2,100
    − 736

8. 6,480
    + 827

9.   7,200
    − 3,300

10. 7,410
    − 680

11.   927
    + 1,294

12.   8,327
    + 13,056

13. 12,256
    − 8,236

14. 12,000
    − 3,000

Complete.

15. 2 yd = _____ in.

16. 30 in. = _____ ft

17. 24 ft = _____ yd

18. $4\frac{3}{4}$ ft = _____ in.

19. 6 yd 2 ft = _____ in.

20. 4 yd = _____ ft

21. 2 yd 2 ft = _____ ft

22. $6\frac{1}{2}$ yd = _____ in.

23. 8 yd $2\frac{1}{2}$ ft = _____ in.

24. 10 in. = _____ ft

25. 9 yd 1 in. = _____ in.

26. 60 in. = _____ ft

Practice Set 3

Use with or after
Lesson 1·7

Write your answers below or on another piece of paper.

As part of a survey, 25 girls and 25 boys were asked what their favorite chore was.

Number of Girls	Number of Boys	Favorite Chore
3	1	Wash dishes
4	4	Make the bed
5	6	Vacuum
5	8	Dust
2	2	Do laundry
6	4	Set the table

1. Make a bar graph to show the results of that survey.

2. Which chore was chosen as the favorite by the most girls? By the most boys?

_____

The students decided to raise money for a field trip by doing chores for people. They earned $1 for each completed chore.

Day of the Week	Money Earned
Sunday	$57
Monday	$44
Tuesday	$39
Wednesday	$46
Thursday	$50
Friday	$61
Saturday	$72

3. Make a broken-line graph showing their earnings for a one-week period.

4. What is the mean, or average, number of dollars that the students earned each day?

_____

Practice Set 3 *continued*

Write your answers below or on another piece of paper.

Solve.

5. 3 * 60 = _____

6. 800 / _____ = 200

7. 150 / 3 = _____

8. _____ * 9 = 630

9. 40 * 80 = _____

10. 2,700 / 30 = _____

11. _____ / 20 = 60

12. 600 * _____ = 6,000

13. 50 * 400 = _____

14. 4,000 / _____ = 80

15. _____ * 60 = 48,000

16. _____ / 70 = 800

17. List in order from greatest to least.

$3\frac{2}{3}$, π, 3.5, $\frac{300}{100}$, $\frac{10}{3}$

_____, _____, _____, _____, _____

Rewrite the numbers, and units, in the following statements so that they sound more reasonable.

> **Example**   Alice said that it takes her about **900 seconds** to get to school in the morning.
>
> Answer: 900 seconds = 15 minutes

18. Richard's report stated that a giraffe can reach leaves on trees as tall as 240 inches.

_____ = _____

19. Greta explained that a hippopotamus can eat 2,080 ounces of food in one night.

_____ = _____

20. Angie made a chart of top running speeds for animals. The entry for the rhinoceros lists its running speed as 158,400 feet/hour.

_____ = _____

21. Allan wrote on a height chart that he is 1,600 millimeters tall.

_____ = _____

Practice Set 4

Use with or after
Lesson 1·8

Write your answers below or on another piece of paper.

The graph below shows the cost of a consultation with a computer specialist. Use the graph to answer the questions.

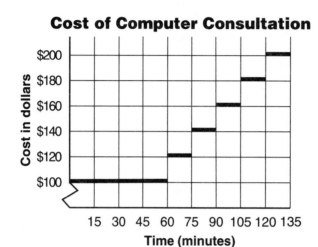

Cost of Computer Consultation

1. What is the cost of the first hour of the consultation? _____

2. After the first hour, what does each additional 15 minutes cost? _____

3. What would be the cost for a consultation lasting 1 hour and

5 minutes? _____

4. What would be the cost for a consultation lasting 2 hours and

15 minutes? _____

$$Radius = \frac{1}{2} * Diameter$$
$$Circumference = \pi * Diameter$$
$$Area = \pi * Radius^2$$

5. Find the radius of the circle. _____

6. Find the circumference. _____

7. Find the area. _____

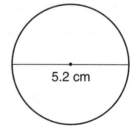

5.2 cm

Practice Set 5

Write your answers below or on another piece of paper.

The student council surveyed students about their favorite school lunch entrees. The results of the survey are displayed in the circle graph.

1. What percent of the students chose pizza?

_____

2. Which lunch entree was chosen by 10% of the students?

_____

3. What percent of the students chose something other than pizza, burrito, or chicken strips?

_____

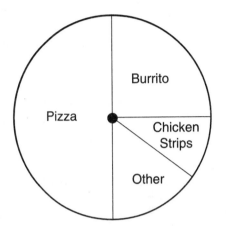

Solve.

4. 46
     * 7

5. 525
      * 6

6. 756
      * 8

7. 827
      * 9

8. 64
     * 73

9. 214
      * 48

10. 519
      * 73

11. 394
      * 15

12. 79 * 29 = _____

13. 143 * 82 = _____

14. 607 * 189 = _____

15. 326 * 160 = _____

List the factors of each number.

16. 18 _____

17. 24 _____

18. 36 _____

19. 50 _____

Practice Set 5 *continued*

Write your answers below or on another piece of paper.

Write the following numbers in digits.

20. forty-three trillion, six hundred eighty-one million, nine hundred

_____

21. two billion, ninety-five million, five hundred thousand

_____

22. six and fourteen-thousandths

_____

Write the following numbers in words.

23. 2.08 _____

24. 836,920,530 _____

25. 65,321,070,000 _____

26. 17,422.7 _____

Determine the balance in each container below and then answer the questions that follow.

Example
Balance = −10
If 16 ⊞ counters are added to the container, what is the new balance?
Balance = +6

10⊞   20⊟

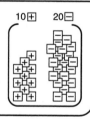

27. What is the balance? _____

28. If 8 ⊟ counters are added to the container, what is the new balance?

_____

25⊞   18⊟

29. What is the balance? _____

30. If 11 ⊞ counters are added to the container, what is the new balance?

_____

17⊞   26⊟

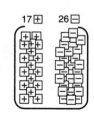

Practice Set 6

Use with or after
Lesson 1·10

Write your answers below or on another piece of paper.

Make name-collection boxes for the three numbers listed below. Use as many different kinds of numbers and operations as you can.

Example

$18\frac{5}{9}$
$\frac{167}{9}$
$19 - \frac{8}{18}$
$9\frac{5}{18} * 2$

1.

13

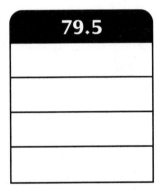

2.

79.5

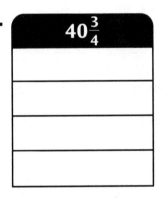

3.

$40\frac{3}{4}$

Find the perimeter and area of each figure.

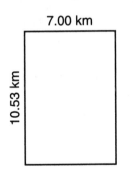

7.00 km

10.53 km

13.9 cm

6.1 cm

4. Perimeter: _____

5. Area: _____

6. Perimeter: _____

7. Area: _____

8. Circle the numbers that are divisible by 3.

543, 544, 545, 546, 547, 548, 549, 550,

551, 552, 553, 554, 555, 556, 557, 558

9

Practice Set 7

Use with or after
Lesson 1·11

Write your answers below or on another piece of paper.

Complete.

1. 1 pint = _____ cups

2. 64 fluid ounces = _____ quarts

3. 6 cups = _____ pints

4. 1 gallon = _____ cups

5. 40 quarts = _____ gallons

6. 48 fluid ounces = _____ cups

7. 3 pints = _____ fluid ounces

8. 12 quarts = _____ pints

Write a number sentence, and then solve.

9. A punch bowl holds 80 fluid ounces. How many pints of juice are needed to fill it?

_____

10. Erika has a half-gallon of milk. How many 6-ounce glasses of milk can she serve? How much milk will be left over?

_____

11. Ron mixed together 3 quarts of juice. How many fluid ounces of juice did he have in all?

_____

Write the missing numbers for the number lines.

12.

    4 ___ ___ ___ ___ 54

13.
    0.3 ___ 0.9 1.2 ___ ___ ___

14.
    0 ___ ___ ___ ___ ___ ___ ___ ___ 1

15.
    0 ___ ___ ___ $1\frac{1}{3}$ ___ 2

Practice Set 7 *continued*

Write your answers below or on another piece of paper.

Write the numbers in standard notation.

16. 3^2 _____   **17.** 2^3 _____   **18.** $\sqrt{100}$ _____   **19.** 10^5 _____

20. 10^0 _____   **21.** 1^4 _____   **22.** 4^2 _____   **23.** $\sqrt{144}$ _____

---

24. Use the clues to complete the puzzle.

_____ _____ _____ _____ . _____

- Divide 27 by 9. Add 1. Write the result in the thousands place.

- Multiply 8 ∗ 7. Subtract half of 100. Write the number in the hundreds place.

- Write the difference between 2^4 and 15 in the tenths place.

- Double the sum of the numbers in the thousands and hundreds place. Divide by 4. Write the result in the ones place.

- Triple the number in the tenths place. Subtract the result from the number in the ones place. Write the result in the tens place.

Divide. Write the result with the remainder.

> **Example** $\overset{21 \rightarrow R27}{37\overline{)804}}$

25. $15\overline{)785}$ **26.** $27\overline{)612}$ **27.** $53\overline{)264}$ **28.** $31\overline{)976}$

29. $18\overline{)629}$ **30.** $22\overline{)320}$ **31.** $63\overline{)892}$ **32.** $16\overline{)701}$

Practice Set 8

Write your answers below or on another piece of paper.

Solve.

1.   9.5
    + 5.6

2.   0.36
    + 0.15

3.   2.23
    − 1.69

4.   5.1
    − 0.82

5.   1.382
    + 6.2

6.   9.47
    − 5.81

7.   0.937
    − 0.324

8.   7.895
    + 4.162

9.   14.85
    − 1.46

10. 9.4 + 7.3 + 2.6 = _____

11. 1.3 + 2.6 + 5.9 = _____

12. 7.4 − 1.89 = _____

13. 5.26 − 3.17 = _____

Write *prime* or *composite* for each number.

14. 12 _____

15. 17 _____

16. 29 _____

17. 46 _____

18. 81 _____

19. 99 _____

Round each number to the nearest thousandth.

20. 9.0716 _____

21. 38.65823 _____

22. 129.9058 _____

23. 74.5309 _____

24. 2.46312 _____

25. 40.5785 _____

Practice Set 8 *continued*

Write your answers below or on another piece of paper.

Solve the pan-balance problems.

26. One coin weighs as much as _____ marbles.

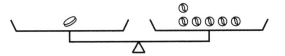

27. One block weighs as much as _____ marbles.

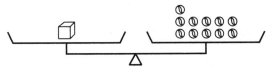

28. One ball weighs as much as _____ marbles.

29. How many marbles would you need to place on the right pan

to balance the two pans? _____

Make name-collection boxes for the numbers below.
Use as many different kinds of numbers and operations as you can.

Example

40.5
81 / 2
32.75 + 7.75
(4 * 9) + 4.5
$\frac{1}{3}$ * 121.5

30. 29.2   **31.** 16.08   **32.** 22.76

Practice Set 9

Use with or after
Lesson 2·5

Write your answers below or on another piece of paper.

Circle the best estimate for each product.

1. 14.9 * 6.7   10   100   1,000

2. 840.5 * 0.4   4   40   400

3. 3.76 * 1.91   8   80   800

4. 78.94 * 0.03   3   30   300

5. 176.4 * 12.4   200   2,000   20,000

6. 783.06 * 1.05   80   800   8,000

Multiply.

7. 9.5
   * 5.6

8. 7.3
   * 0.5

9. 14.9
   * 1.8

10. 26.9
   * 2.3

11. 9.3
   * 0.6

12. 57
   * 3.2

Solve each problem. Then write a number sentence.

13. Alex ordered 3 dozen pens for $1.39 each. What was the total cost of the order, not including tax?

_____

14. Find the area of a square with sides 5.7 cm in length.

_____

Practice Set 9 *continued*

Use with or after
Lesson 2·5

Write your answers below or on another piece of paper.

Complete the "What's My Rule?" tables.

15.

Rule

out = in + 27

in	out
19	
36	
84	
127	
169	

16.

Rule

in	out
31	7
48	24
	29
72	
	56

17.

Rule

in	out
3	90
8	240
10	
	360
20	

18.

Rule

out = in / 8

in	out
24	
	8
720	
	40
4,800	

Solve.

19. When Beth woke up, the temperature was −6°F outside. By the time she got home from school, the temperature was 19°F outside. How many degrees had the temperature risen during the day?

_____

20. The temperature in Milwaukee at 6 P.M. was 28°F. By midnight the temperature had dropped 37 degrees. What was the temperature at midnight?

_____

Practice Set 10

Use with or after
Lesson 2·6

Write your answers below or on another piece of paper.

Multiply.

1. 80 * 0.1 = _____

2. 12 * 0.01 = _____

3. 77 * 0.001 = _____

4. 9.4 * 0.1 = _____

5. 0.06 * 10 = _____

6. 28.6 * 100 = _____

7. 0.7 * 0.1 = _____

8. 40 * 0.01 = _____

9. 3.7 * 1,000 = _____

10. 7.1 * 0.1 = _____

Solve.

11. 1,856 − (320 + 1,105) = _____

12. 78 * (12 − 7) = _____

13. 4,189 + 2,326 + 1,190 = _____

14. 25 + (249 / 3) = _____

15. Mary is having a birthday party. How many $9 pizzas can she buy with $60?

_____

16. Compact disks are on sale for $13 each, including tax. How many CDs can you buy with $55?

_____

Round each number to the nearest tenth.

17. 36.981 _____

18. 8.674 _____

19. 20.85 _____

20. 49.95 _____

21. 17.312 _____

22. 102.56 _____

Measure the line segments to the nearest $\frac{1}{4}$ inch.

23. •———————————————————•

_____ in.

24. •————————————————•

_____ in.

Practice Set 11

Use with or after
Lesson 2·7

Write your answers below or on another piece of paper.

Write the following numbers in standard notation.

1. 6 million _____   **2.** 0.2 billion _____

3. 1.4 trillion _____   **4.** 30 million _____

5. 19 billion _____   **6.** 27.5 million _____

7. 175 million _____   **8.** 4.6 million _____

Write the following numbers in number-and-word notation.

9. 1,300,000 _____

10. 39,000,000 _____

11. 6,000,000,000 _____

12. 12,900,000,000 _____

Complete the "What's My Rule?" tables.

13.

Rule		in	out
out = in / 300			9
			12
			15
		7,500	
			100

14.

Rule		in	out
		7	$\frac{7}{10}$
		10	1
			5
		180	
		100	10

15.

Rule		in	out
out = in − 95		876	
		310	
			95
		190	
			−54

16.

Rule		in	out
		800	16,000
		160	
			900
		315	
		6	120

Practice Set 11 *continued*

Use with or after
Lesson 2·7

Write your answers below or on another piece of paper.

17. Write each fraction as a decimal and a percent.

Fraction	$\frac{1}{2}$	$\frac{1}{4}$	$\frac{1}{5}$	$\frac{1}{10}$	$\frac{3}{4}$	$\frac{7}{10}$	$\frac{1}{3}$	$\frac{7}{8}$
Decimal								
Percent								

Make stem-and-leaf plots for the following groups.

Example	4, 21, 16, 7, 11, 8, 22, 9, 16, 10, 9, 12, 16, 16	Stems (10s)	Leaves (1s)
		0	4, 7, 8, 9, 9
		1	0, 1, 2, 6, 6, 6, 6
		2	1, 2

18. 102, 120, 94, 96, 80, 87, 94, 79, 82, 121, 91, 115, 120, 94, 76

Stems (10s)	Leaves (1s)
7	
8	
9	
10	
11	
12	

19. What is the mode?

_____

20. What is the median?

_____

21. What is the range?

_____

22. 28, 24, 38, 41, 52, 29, 33, 43, 24, 56, 27, 58, 21, 39, 44, 55

Stems (10s)	Leaves (1s)
2	
3	
4	
5	

23. What is the mode?

_____

24. What is the median?

_____

25. What is the range?

_____

Practice Set 12

Use with or after
Lesson 2·8

Write your answers below or on another piece of paper.

Write each number in words.

1. 0.9 _____

2. 1.02 _____

3. 23.015 _____

4. 0.785 _____

5. 0.89 _____

6. 5.0677 _____

Write the digits for each number.

7. seventy-two hundredths _____

8. ninety and six tenths _____

9. one thousand twenty-five and fifteen hundredths _____

10. two and six hundred seventy-five thousandths _____

11. one and two hundred thirty-eight thousandths _____

Use the graph to solve the problems.

12. During training, many athletes eat up to 6,000 calories per day. The recommended diet for most people is 2,000 calories per day. About how many times more calories do athletes eat during training than does the average person?

_____

13. What percent of an athlete's calories comes from fat?

_____

14. How many calories of an athlete's diet come from protein?

_____

15. How many calories come from carbohydrates?

_____

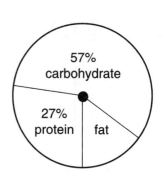

57%
carbohydrate

27%
protein | fat

Practice Set 12 *continued*

Use with or after
Lesson 2·8

Write your answers below or on another piece of paper.

16. Complete the *Powers of 10* table.

The Powers of 10 Table

Thousands	Hundreds	Tens	Ones	.	Tenths	Hundredths	Thousandths
1,000	100			·		0.01	
	10 [10s]		10 [1/10s]	·	10 [1/100s]		10 [1/10,000s]
		10*1	10*1/10	·	10*1/100	10*1/1,000	
10^3			10^0	·	10^{-1}		10^{-3}

Practice Set 13

Use with or after
Lesson 2·9

Write your answers below or on another piece of paper.

Write each number in scientific notation.

1. 5,240,000 _____

2. 10,600,000,000 _____

3. 4,500,000 _____

4. 23,000,000,000 _____

5. 9,000,000,000,000 _____

6. 140,000,000,000 _____

Write each number in standard notation.

7. $3.2 * 10^5$ _____

8. $4.0 * 10^7$ _____

9. $1.23 * 10^8$ _____

10. $6.12 * 10^6$ _____

11. $5.0 * 10^9$ _____

12. $2.5 * 10^{10}$ _____

Write the next three numbers in each pattern.

13. 11, 26, 41, _____, _____, _____

14. 865, 870, 875, _____, _____, _____

15. 44, 56, 68, _____, _____, _____

16. $2\frac{1}{2}$, $2\frac{3}{4}$, 3, _____, _____, _____

17. A number has

    1 in the billions place
    6 in the hundred-thousands place
    4 in the ten-billions place
    2 in the thousands place
    5 in the hundred-millions place
    0 in the rest of the places

    Write the number. _____

Rename as a mixed number.

18. $\frac{21}{2}$ _____

19. $\frac{17}{3}$ _____

20. $\frac{35}{4}$ _____

21. $\frac{20}{9}$ _____

Practice Set 14

Write your answers below or on another piece of paper.

Write each number in scientific notation.

1. 0.0021 _____

2. 0.0009 _____

3. 0.0152 _____

4. 0.702 _____

5. 50 thousand _____

6. 385,000 _____

Write each number in standard notation.

7. $6 * 10^4$ _____

8. $3.6 * 10^{-2}$ _____

9. $8 * 10^{-4}$ _____

10. $2.6 * 10^{-5}$ _____

11. $1.38 * 10^7$ _____

12. $5.8 * 10^6$ _____

Use a calculator to solve. Write the answer in scientific notation.

13. $40^3 * 2^2$ _____

14. $800^2 * 6^3$ _____

15. $60^4 * 7$ _____

16. $90^3 * 10^5$ _____

Answer the questions about the figures below.

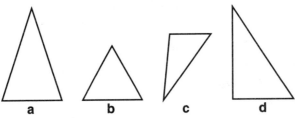

a   b   c   d

17. Which triangle looks like an isosceles triangle? _____

18. Which do you think has a right angle? _____

19. Which looks like an equilateral triangle? _____

20. Which triangle has more than one line of symmetry? _____

Practice Set 15

Use with or after
Lesson 2·11

Write your answers below or on another piece of paper.

Estimate the quotient. Write a number sentence to show how you estimated.

1. 482 / 8 _____

2. 821 / 17 _____

3. 293 / 14 _____

4. 626 / 7 _____

5. 2,762 / 72 _____

6. 1,456 / 29 _____

Solve. Write answers with remainders.

7. 22)8,136

8. 10)4,478

9. 26)1,962

10. 32)714

11. 11)852

12. 5)90

13. Cole has $6.25 to buy school supplies. He wants one pack of pens for $1.15, a folder for $2.67, and a pack of paper for 99¢. How much money will he have left over? Write a number model for this problem.

_____

14. Rosita bought four new books for a total of $32.65. What was the average cost per book?

_____

Answer the following:

15. Find the radius of the circle. _____

16. Find the circumference. _____

17. Find the area. _____

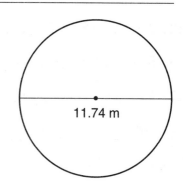

11.74 m

Practice Set 15 continued

Write your answers below or on another piece of paper.

Use the following list of numbers to answer the questions:

14, 18, 19, 13, 20, 13.5, 7.25, 19, 11.25

18. What is the range? _____

19. What is the mode? _____

20. What is the median? _____

21. What is the mean? _____

22. Complete the table.

Product	Exponential Notation	Standard Notation
11 * 11 * 11 * 11		
	$12^{\square}$	1,728
	$\overline{}^{14}$	16,384
	10^{15}	
18 * 18 * 18 * 18 * 18		

23. Write the largest number you can with the following digits:
2, 8, 6, 7, 2, 0, 2, 8, 3, 8, 3, 5, 1, 6, 0

___ ___ ___ ___ ___ ___ ___ ___ ___ ___ ___ ___ ___ ___ ___

Add parentheses to the number sentences to make them correct.

24. $250 = 10 * 57 - 32$

25. $6 * 12 + 8 - 3 = 102$

26. $521 = 11 * 19 + 312$

27. $12 * 30 - 5 = 300$

28. $4.8 + 2.2 - 5 = 2$

29. $7.25 + 1.25 * 2 + 4.25 = 14$

30. $56 / 2.3 + 5.7 * 12 = 84$

Name _____ Date _____ Time _____

Practice Set 16

Use with or after
Lesson 2-12

SRB
216–217
241 262

Write your answers below or on another piece of paper.

Estimate each quotient. Write a number sentence to show how you estimated.

1. 14.4 / 3 _____

2. 83.6 / 4 _____

3. 47.72 / 11 _____

4. 33.1 / 7 _____

5. 89.7 / 9 _____

6. 52.6 / 6 _____

Divide. Round to the nearest hundredth.

7. 29 / 7 _____

8. 35 / 3 _____

9. 51 / 9 _____

10. 70 / 8 _____

11. 64 / 6 _____

12. 47 / 9 _____

Triangle: Area = $\frac{1}{2}$ * base * height
Parallelogram: Area = base * height

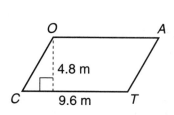

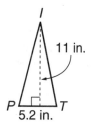

13. What is the name of the figure?

_____

14. What is its area?

_____

15. What is the name of the figure?

_____

16. What is its area?

_____

25

Practice Set 16 continued

Use with or after
Lesson 2·11

Write your answers below or on another piece of paper.

Write the words for the following numbers.

17. 62,093,070 _____

18. 11,263,750,000,000 _____

19. 49,034,520,000,000 _____

20. 560.8034 _____

Complete the number lines.

21.

4 ___ ___ 52 ___ ___ ___ 116

22.

$\frac{11}{16}$ ___ ___ ___ ___ $\frac{16}{16}$ or 1

23.

−82 ___ ___ ___ ___ ___ −70

Complete.

24. $2^8 = $ _____

25. $4^{\square} = 256$

26. $8 * 8 * 8 * 8 * 8 * 8 = 8^{\square}$

27. The square root of 256 = _____.

28. y to the third power $= y^{\square}$

Draw the next picture.

29.

30.

Practice Set 17

Use with or after
Lesson 3·1

Write your answers below or on another piece of paper.

Write the letter of the special case which matches each general pattern.

1. $a(3 + 7) = (a * 3) + (a * 7)$ _____   **A.** $7^3 = 7 * 7 * 7$

2. $n^3 = n * n * n$ _____   **B.** $3(21 - 5) = (3 * 21) - 15$

3. $a + 0 = a$ _____   **C.** $17 + 2 = 2 + 17$

4. $x + 2 = 2 + x$ _____   **D.** $5(3 + 7) = (5 * 3) + (5 * 7)$

5. $3(x - 5) = 3x - 15$ _____   **E.** $\frac{1}{5} + \frac{1}{5} = \frac{2}{5}$

6. $\frac{1}{x} + \frac{1}{x} = \frac{2}{x}$ _____   **F.** $42 + 0 = 42$

Solve. (You may use a calculator for Problems 7–12.)

7. $6^5 * 1^5 =$ _____   **8.** $7^2 - 2^3 =$ _____

9. $9^2 - 3^3 =$ _____   **10.** $14^2 + 10^3 =$ _____

11. $20^2 * 2^4 =$ _____   **12.** $2^{24} - 24^2 =$ _____

13. $6^3 / 6^2 =$ _____   **14.** $8^2 * 8^3 = 8^{\boxed{}}$

15. Charlotte earns $6.00 per week for mowing two neighbors' lawns. She pays her brother Sam 50¢ to pick up grass clippings for compost. After she pays her brother, how much money will she make in 7 weeks?

_____

16. Suppose Charlotte doubled the number of lawns she mowed and also doubled the amount she earned in a week. Should she increase the amount she gives her brother, and if so, by how much? Explain.

_____

_____

_____

27

Practice Set 18

Write your answers below or on another piece of paper.

For each set of special cases, write a number sentence with two variables to describe the general pattern.

1. $3(15 + 9) = (3 * 15) + (3 * 9)$
$3(5 + 1) = (3 * 5) + (3 * 1)$
$3(0.25 + 0.75) = (3 * 0.25) + (3 * 0.75)$

_____

2. $10 * (2 * 4) = 2 * (10 * 4)$
$10 * (8 * 5) = 8 * (10 * 5)$
$10 * (0.3 * 0.8) = 0.3 * (10 * 0.8)$

_____

3. $0.4(1.05 - 3) = (0.4 * 1.05) - (0.4 * 3)$
$0.4(5.23 - 1.7) = (0.4 * 5.23) - (0.4 * 1.7)$
$0.4(17 - 6) = (0.4 * 17) - (0.4 * 6)$

_____

Use digits to write the following numbers:

4. nine and twenty-three hundredths _____

5. sixteen and four-ninths _____

6. eleven and four hundred eighteen thousandths _____

Complete each pattern. Note: There may be more than one operation per pattern set.

7. 12, 15, 11, 14, _____, _____, 9

8. _____, _____, 46, 36, 26, _____, _____

9. 54, 59, 67, _____, 80, _____, _____, _____

10. 29, 34, 39, _____, 49, _____, _____

11. 14, _____, 16, 8, 18, _____, _____, 12

Practice Set 18 *continued*

Use with or after
Lesson 3·2

Write your answers below or on another piece of paper.

Solve.

12.   59
       * 59

13. 33)835

14.   28
       * 25

15. 71)390

16. 97)4,598

17. 6)395

18.   200
       * 56

19. 46)3,318

20. Coach Rivera wants to put the 76 sixth graders in teams for a volleyball tournament. How many teams of 9 can he form?

_____

21. Javier was married at the age of 28. In 3 more years, he will have been married 25 years. How old is Javier?

_____

Complete.

22. 10^{10} = _____

23. $10^{\square}$ = 10,000,000,000,000

24. 100 * 100 * 100 * 100 * 100 = $10^{\square}$

25. 10 * 10^2 = $10^{\square}$ = _____

Round each number to the nearest thousandth.

26. 3.9025 _____   **27.** 78.2953 _____

28. 3.2871 _____   **29.** 6.0208 _____

30. 3.4798 _____   **31.** 26.2149 _____

Tell whether each number is *prime* or *composite*.

32. 31 _____   **33.** 57 _____   **34.** 111 _____   **35.** 19 _____

Practice Set 19

Write your answers below or on another piece of paper.

Write an algebraic expression for each situation. Use the suggested variable.

1. Virginia has 7 more rubber stamps than Melinda. If Melinda has r rubber stamps, how many rubber stamps does Virginia have?

_____

2. Marco's dog weighs p pounds. Cody's dog weighs 5 pounds less. How much does Cody's dog weigh?

_____

3. On Monday, Ellen sold 3 pumpkins. The next day she sold m more pumpkins. How many did she sell in all?

_____

Write *true* or *false* for each number sentence.

4. $(3 + 4) * 3 = 21$ _____

5. $42 = (54 / 9) * 7$ _____

6. $7 * (6 + 3) = (40 / 5) * (17 - 9)$ _____

7. $(48 / 8) / 2 < 10$ _____

8. $(7 * 8) - 3 = 55$ _____

Solve.

9.	10.	11.	12.
905 − 238	847 − 460	957 − 249	3,688 + 9,375

13.	14.	15.	16.
85,387 + 47,967	9,651 − 850	381 + 429	2,109 + 762

17. $15,038 - 27,864 =$ _____

18. $9,080 + 799 + 225 =$ _____

19. $90 + 569 + 77 =$ _____

20. $4,896 - (658 + 1,900) =$ _____

Practice Set 20

Use with or after
Lesson 3·4

Write your answers below or on another piece of paper.

Complete the "What's My Rule?" tables.

1.

Rule
out = in * 4

in	out
60	240
16	
	340
11	
	142

2.

Rule
0.3 * in = out

in	out
30	9
	0.15
105	
393	
705	

3.

Rule
in − 175 = out

in	out
600	
112	
	35
10	
	−82

4.

Rule

in	out
8	16
14	28
	45
35	
40.2	80.4

Rename as a fraction.

5. $6\frac{1}{5}$ _____

6. $3\frac{3}{8}$ _____

7. $4\frac{1}{2}$ _____

8. $1\frac{16}{24}$ _____

9. $10\frac{12}{13}$ _____

10. $5\frac{2}{5}$ _____

11. $7\frac{2}{9}$ _____

12. $24\frac{2}{3}$ _____

13. $10\frac{2}{5}$ _____

14. $4\frac{6}{7}$ _____

15. $21\frac{3}{5}$ _____

16. $14\frac{1}{6}$ _____

17. $18\frac{1}{9}$ _____

18. $9\frac{1}{3}$ _____

19. $11\frac{1}{8}$ _____

20. $3\frac{14}{15}$ _____

Practice Set 20 *continued*

Use with or after
Lesson 3·4

Write your answers below or on another piece of paper.

Estimate each product. Write a number sentence to show how you estimated.

21. 12.3 * 5.6 _____   **22.** 1.35 * 27.9 _____

23. 261.95 * 32.8 _____   **24.** 2.39 * 682 _____

25. 86.74 * 4.18 _____   **26.** 126.9 * 4.56 _____

27. 7.893 * 12.008 _____   **28.** 981 * 1.73 _____

Answer the following questions:

29. Which is the prime factorization of 24?

   2 * 3 * 5   2 * 2 * 2 * 3   2 * 12   2 * 2 * 3 * 3

30. Which is the prime factorization of 72?

   2 * 5 * 5   2 * 36   2 * 2 * 2 * 3 * 3

31. Which is the prime factorization of 77?

   2 * 5 * 7   3 * 3 * 3 * 3   7 * 11   2 * 6 * 6

32. What are the prime factors for 105?

   _____

33. What number is represented by the prime factors 3 * 5 * 5 * 13?

   _____

Use the following list of numbers to answer the questions.

   10, 8.5, 11, 9, 10.5, 10.5, 7, 13, 10.5

34. What is the range? _____   **35.** What is the mode? _____

36. What is the median? _____   **37.** What is the mean? _____

38. If you disregard the highest and lowest numbers, how would that affect the mean? Do you think this would be a *more* or *less* accurate representation of the numbers? Explain.

   _____

   _____

   _____

Practice Set 21

Write your answers below or on another piece of paper.

Complete the rate tables below. Then answer the questions.

Example A company can produce 800 widgets per day.

widgets	800	1,600	2,400	3,200	4,000
days	1	2	3	4	5

---

1. How many widgets can the factory produce in $3\frac{1}{2}$ days? _____

2. How many 5-day weeks will it take to produce 16,000 widgets? _____

On the highway, Alec's car gets 28 miles per gallon of gasoline.

3.

miles	28					…	
gallons	1	2	3	4	5	…	12

4. His parent's house is 100 miles away by the nearest highway. How many gallons of gasoline will Alec need to get there?

_____

5. The gas tank holds 12 gallons. How many times will Alec need to stop for gas on a road trip of 340 miles?

_____

In the city, Alec's car gets 23 miles per gallon of gasoline.

6.

miles	23					…	
gallons	1	2	3	4	5	…	12

7. How far can the car go in the city on 4.25 gallons? _____

8. Alec drives about 425 miles in the city each month. How many gallons does he buy in a month?

_____

33

Practice Set 21 *continued*

Write your answers below or on another piece of paper.

Find the landmarks for the following set of numbers:

4, 3, 6, 2.5, 3, 2.25, 1.5, 7, 4, 6.75

9. maximum _____

10. minimum _____

11. range _____

12. median _____

13. mean _____

14. mode _____

Solve.

15. $9 * 10^{-2}$ = _____

16. $50 * 10^{\square} = 0.5$

17. $54 = 10^{\square} * 0.054$

18. $42,000 = 7 * 6 * 10^{\square}$

19. $10^{\square} * 1,500 = 0.15$

20. $10^{\square} * 8,306 = 0.8306$

Round to the nearest million.

21. 386,905,817,009 _____

22. 9,632,928,025 _____

23. 65,837,296,702 _____

24. 9,027,583 _____

25. 782,660,327 _____

26. 2,396,920,275 _____

Write each number in standard notation.

27. 0.5 million _____

28. 700 thousand _____

29. 1.9 billion _____

30. 5.2 trillion _____

31. 67 billion _____

32. 100 trillion _____

33. 3 million _____

34. 0.2 trillion _____

Practice Set 22

Use with or after
Lesson 3·7

Write your answers below or on another piece of paper.

Use the spreadsheet to answers questions 1−4.

1. What is in cell A2? _____

2. What is in cell B4? _____

3. Which cell contains the word "Total"?

_____

4. Write a formula for calculating cell B8
that uses the cell names.

_____

	Records	
	A	**B**
1	Day	Sales
2	Monday	$4.25
3	Tuesday	$9.50
4	Wednesday	$8.25
5	Thursday	$6.50
6	Friday	$12.75
7		
8	Total	$41.25

Find the least common multiple for each pair of numbers.

5. 8, 10 _____   **6.** 2, 7 _____   **7.** 9, 12 _____

8. 5, 6 _____   **9.** 10, 15 _____   **10.** 9, 15 _____

Solve. Write answers with remainders for division problems.

11. 4)‾496‾   **12.** 6)‾283‾   **13.** 8)‾2,419‾   **14.** 323
                                                           * 8

15. 687   **16.** 5)‾325‾   **17.** 44)‾505‾   **18.** 784
     * 12   − 531

19. 1,026   **20.** 36)‾623‾   **21.** 5)‾225‾   **22.** 825
     − 296   + 369

Practice Set 23

Use with or after
Lesson 3·8

Write your answers below or on another piece of paper.

Add.

1. 7 + (−6) = _____

2. 19 + (−7) = _____

3. −11 + (−5) = _____

4. 9 + (−4) = _____

5. 8 + (−9) = _____

6. −14 + (−2) = _____

7. −20 + 7 = _____

8. −12 + (−12) = _____

Find the greatest common factor for each pair of numbers.

9. 12, 30 _____

10. 6, 16 _____

11. 16, 24 _____

12. 18, 29 _____

13. 21, 15 _____

14. 32, 50 _____

Ellen made a table of sales from her farm stand.

15. Make a broken-line graph showing the sales for Weeks 1−6.

16. Which week had the greatest sales?

_____

17. What were the sales for Week 1?

_____

18. How much greater were the sales for Week 6 than for Week 1?

_____

19. What was the mean number of dollars for the 6 weeks?

_____

Week	Sales
1	$150
2	$250
3	$300
4	$325
5	$350
6	$275

Practice Set 23 *continued*

Use with or after
Lesson 3·8

Write your answers below or on another piece of paper.

Solve.

20. 1,254
    $* 50$
	21. 4,235
	    $- 1,227$
		22. 1,675
		    $- 885$
			23. 8,263
			    $+ 7,582$

24. 82.4
    $+ 33.9$
	25. 11.7
	    $- 18.5$
		26. 500
		    $* 7.6$
			27. 5,345
			    $- 4,226$

28. 4,321
    $- 2,636$
	29. 71.4
	    $+ 22.8$
		30. 30.9
		    $- 18.4$
			31. 22.8
			    $* 11$

Complete the number lines.

32.
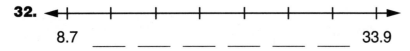
8.7 ___ ___ ___ ___ ___ ___ 33.9

33.
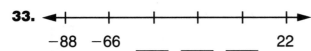
−88 −66 ___ ___ ___ 22

34.

71 ___ ___ ___ ___ ___ 419

35.
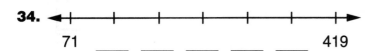
3.1 ___ ___ ___ 5.1

Solve.

> Volume = length * width * height
> = Area * height

Each rectangular prism has a volume of 60 cubic inches. What is the height of each prism?

36.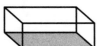

Area of base = 12 in.^{2}

Height = _____

37.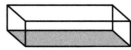

Area of base = 15 in.^{2}

Height = _____

37

Practice Set 24

Use with or after
Lesson 3·9

Write your answers below or on another piece of paper.

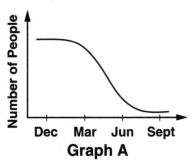

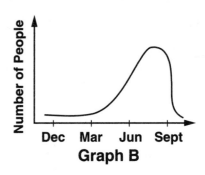

Write the letter of the graph that best fits the description.

1. This graph represents the number of people

who are camping at a state beach park in California. _____

2. This graph represents the number of people

who are staying at a ski resort in New Hampshire. _____

The perimeter of a square can be found by the formula $p = 4 * s$**. Find the perimeter of a square with**

3. $s = 7$ inches _____

4. $s = 3.5$ meters _____

5. $s = 0.2$ kilometers _____

6. $s = 2\frac{1}{2}$ miles _____

Use the numbers from 100 to 120 to answer the following questions.

7. Which numbers are divisible by 5? _____

8. Which numbers are divisible by 3? _____

9. Which numbers are divisible by 6? _____

10. Which numbers are prime? _____

Practice Set 24 *continued*

Use with or after
Lesson 3·9

Write your answers below or on another piece of paper.

Complete the "What's My Rule?" tables.

11.

Rule		in	out
		$54\frac{1}{2}$	$46\frac{1}{4}$
		29	$20\frac{3}{4}$
			$88\frac{1}{2}$
		$38\frac{5}{8}$	

12.

Rule		in	out
in $* 10^{-2}$ = out		78.3	0.783
		480	
			3.65
		14	

Add parentheses to the number sentences to make them correct.

13. $8.4 = 7 * 2 - 0.8$

14. $336 - 26 - 29 = 339$

15. $7 * 3.4 + 5 = 58.8$

16. $7 * 3.4 + 5 = 28.8$

17. Use the clues to complete the puzzle.

_____ _____ _____ . _____ _____ _____

- Add 53 and 37. Divide by 10 and write the result in the ones place.
- Quadruple the number in the ones place and divide by 6. Write the result in the tenths place.
- Multiply 31 $*$ 8. Subtract 241. Write the result in the thousandths place.
- Subtract the number in the tenths place from 54 and divide by 6. Write the result in the hundredths place.
- Find $\frac{5}{8}$ of 8. Write the result in the tens place.
- Subtract the product of 6 $*$ 16 from 100. Write the result in the hundreds place.

Practice Set 25

Use with or after
Lesson 4·1

Write your answers below or on another piece of paper.

Write each fraction in simplest form.

1. $\frac{6}{12}$ _____

2. $\frac{75}{100}$ _____

3. $\frac{4}{6}$ _____

4. $\frac{2}{8}$ _____

5. $\frac{10}{24}$ _____

6. $\frac{26}{50}$ _____

7. $\frac{5}{15}$ _____

8. $\frac{18}{24}$ _____

Compare. Write <, >, or =.

9. $6 * 10^5$ _____ 600,000

10. $1.25 * 10^{-2}$ _____ 0.25

11. 9.5 million _____ 950,000

12. $3 * 10^7$ _____ 3,500,000

13. $5.23 * 10^7$ _____ 53 billion

14. 0.057 _____ $5.7 * 10^{-3}$

Find the volume of each rectangular prism.

15.

4.75 cm
2 cm
3.5 cm

Volume: _____

16.

3 ft
6 ft
$2\frac{1}{2}$ ft

Volume: _____

17.

4 in.
5.25 in.
4 in.

Volume: _____

18.

3.5 yd
3.5 yd
3.5 yd

Volume: _____

Solve.

19. $(-43) + (-98) = y$

20. $(+264) + (-154) = J$

21. $r + (+153) = (-632)$

22. $M = (-25) + (-84)$

Practice Set 26

Use with or after Lesson 4·2

Write your answers below or on another piece of paper.

Compare. Write <, >, or =.

1. $\frac{1}{6}$ _____ $\frac{2}{5}$

2. $\frac{2}{3}$ _____ $\frac{5}{8}$

3. $\frac{2}{9}$ _____ $\frac{7}{12}$

4. $\frac{3}{10}$ _____ $\frac{1}{4}$

5. $\frac{5}{12}$ _____ $\frac{10}{24}$

6. $\frac{1}{4}$ _____ $\frac{3}{7}$

7. $\frac{8}{9}$ _____ $\frac{9}{11}$

8. $\frac{5}{25}$ _____ $\frac{1}{5}$

Add, using mental math.

9. $-5 + 7 =$ _____

10. $-20 + 6 =$ _____

11. $15 + (-8) =$ _____

12. $-3 + (-7) =$ _____

13. $10 + (-17) =$ _____

14. $-6 + 9 =$ _____

15. $-5 + -4 =$ _____

16. $-9 + -6 =$ _____

Complete the "What's My Rule?" tables.

17.

Rule		in	out
in = out * 2.5		565	
		830	
		277.5	
			17
		90	

18.

Rule		in	out
out = in / 9		369	
		837	
			19
		2,304	
			44

Practice Set 27

Use with or after
Lesson 4·3

Write your answers below or on another piece of paper.

Add or subtract. Write your answers as fractions in simplest form.

1. $\frac{1}{3} + \frac{5}{12} =$ _____

2. $\frac{5}{6} - \frac{1}{12} =$ _____

3. $\frac{7}{8} - \frac{3}{16} =$ _____

4. $\frac{1}{2} + \frac{1}{10} =$ _____

5. $\frac{3}{10} + \frac{4}{5} =$ _____

6. $\frac{11}{12} - \frac{1}{6} =$ _____

7. $\frac{1}{2} + \frac{1}{2} + \frac{1}{4} =$ _____

8. $\frac{3}{5} + \frac{1}{2} + \frac{1}{10} =$ _____

9. Complete the table.

Words	Standard Notation	Exponential Notation
one-tenth	0.1	10^{-1}
	0.01	
one-thousandth		
one-millionth		
		10^{-9}
one-trillionth		

According to the graph:

10. Which season is preferred by Mr. Crowder's class?

_____

11. What percent of the class does NOT prefer spring?

_____

Practice Set 27 *continued*

Use with or after
Lesson 4·3

SRB
13–24
102

Write your answers below or on another piece of paper.

Solve.

12.   82,416
      + 15,249

13.   6,375
        * 53

14.   233
        * 61

15.   5.83
        * 4.2

16.   9.457
      − 3.363

17.   3.907
      − 1.478

18.   43
        * 2.6

19.   33.90
      + 12.05

20.   1.907
      + 90.640

21.   634.98
      − 112.90

22. 3)1.80

23. 8)71.2

24. 9)40.5

25.   18,323
      + 21,475

26.   9.76
        * 7.3

27.   167.06
        * 0.04

Fill in the missing numbers on the number lines.

28.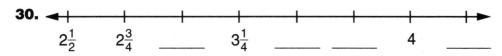

−0.25   −0.23   _____   −0.19   _____   _____   −0.13   _____

29.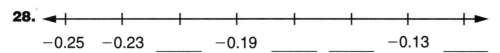

_____   7   _____   15   19   _____   _____   _____

30.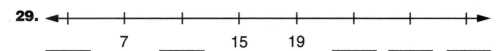

$2\frac{1}{2}$ $2\frac{3}{4}$ _____ $3\frac{1}{4}$ _____   _____   4   _____

31.

$-\frac{16}{8}$ $-\frac{15}{8}$ _____ $-\frac{13}{8}$ _____   _____   _____   _____

32.

101.5   101.8   102.1   _____   _____   _____   103.3   _____

33.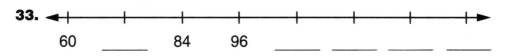

60   _____   84   96   _____   _____   _____

43

Practice Set 28

Write your answers below or on another piece of paper.

Add or subtract.

1. $4\frac{1}{5}$
   $+ 3\frac{2}{5}$

2. 6
   $- 1\frac{1}{4}$

3. $10\frac{1}{6}$
   $- 4\frac{5}{6}$

4. $2\frac{1}{8}$
   $+ 1\frac{7}{8}$

5. $7\frac{2}{3}$
   $+ 4\frac{2}{3}$

6. $9\frac{1}{4}$
   $- 6\frac{3}{4}$

7. $5\frac{1}{3}$
   $- 1\frac{1}{3}$

8. 10
   $+ 2\frac{2}{7}$

9. $8\frac{1}{5}$
   $- 2\frac{3}{5}$

Find the missing number.

10. $\frac{2}{3} = \frac{a}{30}$ _____

11. $\frac{5}{12} = \frac{x}{48}$ _____

12. $\frac{7}{10} = \frac{c}{50}$ _____

13. $\frac{7}{25} = \frac{d}{100}$ _____

14. $\frac{5}{6} = \frac{r}{42}$ _____

15. $\frac{2}{9} = \frac{t}{45}$ _____

Determine the balance in each container below.

16. What is the balance? _____

17. If 18 ⊟ counters are added to the container, what is

the new balance? _____

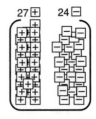

18. What is the balance? _____

19. If 7 ⊞ counters are removed from the container,

what is the new balance? _____

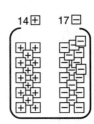

Practice Set 29

Write your answers below or on another piece of paper.

Add or subtract.

1. $\quad 7$
$\quad - 4\frac{2}{3}$

2. $\quad 9\frac{1}{5}$
$\quad - 8\frac{8}{10}$

3. $\quad 1\frac{1}{2}$
$\quad + 6\frac{3}{4}$

4. $\quad 5\frac{5}{6}$
$\quad - 2\frac{7}{12}$

5. $\quad 2\frac{5}{8}$
$\quad + 2\frac{1}{4}$

6. $\quad 7\frac{2}{3}$
$\quad + 6\frac{3}{4}$

7. $8\frac{1}{5} - 6\frac{3}{10} =$ _____

8. $4\frac{1}{5} - 2\frac{1}{2} =$ _____

9. $2\frac{1}{3} + 1\frac{1}{6} + 4\frac{1}{2} =$ _____

10. $5\frac{3}{8} + 3\frac{1}{4} + 1\frac{1}{2} =$ _____

Identify each angle. Write _acute, right, obtuse, reflex,_ or _straight_.

11. 290° angle _____

12. 37° angle _____

13. 135° angle _____

14. 180° angle _____

15. 90° angle _____

16. 75° angle _____

Complete each pattern. Note: There may be more than one operation per pattern set.

17. 5, 7, 11, 13, _____, _____, 23

18. _____, _____, 4.6, 3.6, 2.6, _____, _____

19. 54, 59, 57, _____, 60, _____, _____, _____

20. 2.9, 3.4, 3.9, _____, 4.9, _____, _____

21. 50, _____, 34, 22, 18, _____, _____, −10

Practice Set 29 *continued*

Use with or after
Lesson 4·5

Write your answers below or on another piece of paper.

Simplify the fractions.

22. $\frac{4}{14}$ _____

23. $\frac{11}{121}$ _____

24. $\frac{14}{6}$ _____

25. $\frac{70}{100}$ _____

26. $\frac{8}{48}$ _____

27. $\frac{3}{18}$ _____

28. $\frac{4}{6}$ _____

29. $\frac{6}{1}$ _____

30. $\frac{9}{12}$ _____

31. $\frac{404}{808}$ _____

32. $\frac{14}{16}$ _____

33. $\frac{36}{22}$ _____

Solve.

34.   563
     * 14

35.   51
     * 63

36.   642
     * 53

37.   58,225
     + 16,745

38.   10,345
     + 4,389

39.   155,000
     + 34,500

40.   899
     − 76

41.   440
     − 105

Answer the following.

> Radius = $\frac{1}{2}$ * Diameter
> Circumference = π * Diameter
> Area = π * Radius^2

42. Find the radius of the circle. _____

43. Find the circumference. _____

44. Find the area. _____

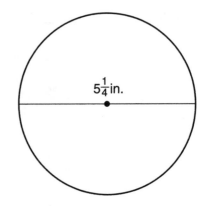

$5\frac{1}{4}$ in.

Practice Set 30

Use with or after
Lesson 4·6

Write your answers below or on another piece of paper.

Multiply. Write the answer in simplest form.

1. $\frac{4}{5} * \frac{1}{2} =$ _____

2. $\frac{3}{8} * \frac{1}{6} =$ _____

3. $6 * \frac{3}{10} =$ _____

4. $\frac{7}{9} * \frac{1}{6} =$ _____

5. $\frac{1}{3} * \frac{1}{3} =$ _____

6. $4 * \frac{1}{8} =$ _____

7. $\frac{4}{7} * \frac{1}{4} =$ _____

8. $\frac{7}{15} * \frac{1}{2} =$ _____

Round to the nearest thousandth.

9. 8.2758 _____

10. 10.0756 _____

11. 3.7907 _____

12. 42.9374 _____

13. 0.2898 _____

14. Is point (29,43) above, below, or on the line through points A and B?

_____

15. Is point (50,30) above, below, or on the line through points A and B?

_____

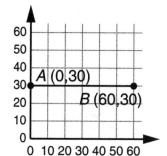

16. Is point (55,16) to the left of, to the right of, or on the line through points A and B?

_____

17. Is point (35,35) to the left of, to the right of, or on the line through points A and B?

_____

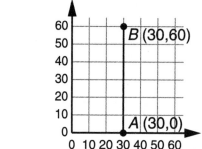

Practice Set 31

Write your answers below or on another piece of paper.

Multiply.

1. $2\frac{1}{3} * \frac{1}{5} =$ _____

2. $3\frac{1}{6} * 7 =$ _____

3. $4\frac{2}{3} * 2\frac{1}{3} =$ _____

4. $5\frac{1}{2} * 3\frac{3}{8} =$ _____

5. $6\frac{5}{6} * 3\frac{1}{3} =$ _____

6. $2\frac{3}{4} * 7\frac{1}{2} =$ _____

Divide. Round to the nearest hundredth.

7. $92 / 7 =$ _____

8. $55 / 6 =$ _____

9. $128 / 9 =$ _____

10. $89 / 4 =$ _____

11. $100 / 18 =$ _____

12. $155 / 12 =$ _____

Measure each angle to the nearest degree.

13. _____ °

14. _____ °

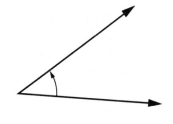

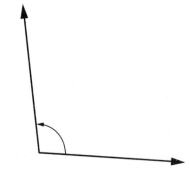

Practice Set 31 *continued*

Use with or after
Lesson 4·7

Write your answers below or on another piece of paper.

Complete the number lines.

15. 1.4 ____ 6.2 ____ ____ ____ 15.8

16. 118 ____ ____ ____ ____ 438

17. $8\frac{4}{5}$ ____ $19\frac{1}{5}$ ____ ____ $34\frac{4}{5}$

18. −24 ____ ____ ____ 0

Write >, <, or = to make each sentence true.

19. 210.5 _____ 3,376 / 16

20. 72 + 129 _____ 5 * 39

21. 25% of 356 _____ 115 * $\frac{7}{2}$

22. 3,144 − 1,938 _____ 35^2

Write in standard notation.

23. $\sqrt{9}$ _____ **24.** $\sqrt{144}$ _____

25. $\sqrt{81}$ _____ **26.** $\sqrt{25}$ _____

27. $\sqrt{121}$ _____ **28.** $\sqrt{49}$ _____

Solve.

29. $\frac{1}{3}$ of 51 _____ **30.** $\frac{2}{3}$ of 84 _____

31. $\frac{2}{7}$ of 91 _____ **32.** $\frac{5}{8}$ of 240 _____

33. $\frac{2}{7}$ of 98 _____ **34.** $\frac{7}{11}$ of 143 _____

Practice Set 32

Write your answers below or on another piece of paper.

Write the missing numbers for the table.

1.

Fraction	Decimal	Percent
		58%
$\frac{6}{18}$		
	0.5	
	0.32	
$\frac{7}{8}$		
		8%

Evaluate the following algebraic expressions for $c = 9.3$ and $d = 20$.

2. $c + 1$

_____

3. $c - 1.5$

_____

4. $c / 3$

_____

5. $c + 10.6$

_____

6. $c * 4.6$

_____

7. $15 - c$

_____

8. $3d - 1$

_____

9. $2d + 6.5$

_____

10. $d + d$

_____

11. $200 / d$

_____

12. $d - (3 * 2)$

_____

13. d^3

_____

Compare. Write < or >.

14. $\frac{1}{7}$ _____ $\frac{1}{6}$

15. $\frac{3}{8}$ _____ $\frac{8}{3}$

16. $\frac{2}{4}$ _____ $\frac{2}{12}$

17. $\frac{2}{11}$ _____ $\frac{5}{50}$

18. $\frac{7}{10}$ _____ $\frac{12}{25}$

19. $\frac{1}{9}$ _____ $\frac{2}{24}$

Practice Set 32 *continued*

Use with or after
Lesson 4·9

Write your answers below or on another piece of paper.

Write the missing numbers for the table.

20.

Product	Exponential Notation	Standard Notation
	9^3	
	$12^{\square}$	144
	10^6	
$\frac{1}{10} * \frac{1}{10} * \frac{1}{10} * \frac{1}{10}$	$10^{\square}$	

Solve.

21. $a = 7 - 14$

22. $32 - 66 = b$

23. $4 - 18 = c$

24. $39 - 47 = d$

25. $-15 - 73 = e$

26. $-900 + 30 = f$

27. $g = 29 - 600$

28. $h = 230 - 35$

29. $45 - 92 = i$

30. $45 - 39 = j$

31. $70 - 30 = k$

32. $50 - 80 = l$

33. $2 - 18 = m$

34. $12 - 77 = n$

Complete the number lines.

35.

21 ___ ___ ___ 105

36.

$19\frac{1}{3}$ 27 ___ ___ ___ $57\frac{2}{3}$

37.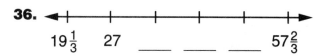

-28 ___ ___ -19 -16 ___

51

Practice Set 33

Use with or after
Lesson 4·10

Write your answers below or on another piece of paper.

The fourth, fifth, and sixth grades at Apple Valley Elementary sell magazine subscriptions to raise money for field trips.

1. How many magazine subscriptions have been sold in all?

_____

2. What percent has been sold by

  a. the fourth grade _____

  b. the fifth grade _____

  c. the sixth grade _____

3. Make a circle graph of the data.

Magazine Subscription Sales	
Grade	**Number of Subscriptions Sold**
Fourth	42
Fifth	36
Sixth	72

Complete.

4. $5 * 10^4 = $ _____

5. $5^{\square} = 25$

6. $80{,}000{,}000 = $ _____ $* 10^7$

7. $3^4 = 8.1 * 10^{\square}$

8. $6.4 * 10^{\square} = 64{,}000$

9. $45 * 10^{-4} = $ _____

10. $3.14 * 10^{\square} = 314{,}000{,}000{,}000$

11. $6 * 10^{\square} = 0.0006$

12. $8.94 * 10^7 = $ _____

13. $943 * 10^{-9} = $ _____

Round 74,082,729,253 to the nearest

14. million _____

15. ten thousand _____

16. hundred thousand _____

17. billion _____

Practice Set 33 *continued*

Use with or after
Lesson 4·10

Write your answers below or on another piece of paper.

Solve.

18. $26\overline{)416}$

19. $\begin{array}{r} 736 \\ *\ 25 \\ \hline \end{array}$

20. $45\overline{)3,105}$

21. $\begin{array}{r} 11,953 \\ -\ 10,635 \\ \hline \end{array}$

22. $24\overline{)2,496}$

23. $\begin{array}{r} 118 \\ *\ 7 \\ \hline \end{array}$

24. $\begin{array}{r} 523 \\ -\ 153 \\ \hline \end{array}$

25. $\begin{array}{r} 5,835 \\ -\ 5,823 \\ \hline \end{array}$

26. $\begin{array}{r} 1291 \\ +\ 412 \\ \hline \end{array}$

27. $\begin{array}{r} 85,431 \\ +\ 56,432 \\ \hline \end{array}$

28. $(145 \div 5) * 40$

29. $165 - (16 * 9) =$ _____

30. $25 * 25 * 18 =$ _____

31. The temperature at noon was 33°C. The highest temperature that day was 5°C warmer; the lowest was 6°C cooler. What was the temperature range that day?

_____

32. The first temperature reading was 37°F. The second reading showed that the temperature had dropped 13°F. The third reading showed another 13-degree drop. What's the temperature at the third reading?

_____

Complete the "What's My Rule?" tables.

33.

Rule		in	out
in = out * $\frac{5}{8}$		$\frac{5}{40}$ or $\frac{1}{8}$	$\frac{1}{5}$
			$\frac{1}{4}$
			80
		$\frac{15}{32}$	
			$\frac{1}{3}$

34.

Rule		in	out
		786	79
		638	−69
			18
		1,034	
		210	−497

Practice Set 34

Write your answers below or on another piece of paper.

The Perfect Look Boutique is having a sale. These signs are posted in the store.

Jeans
$5 off

Sweaters
20% off

T-shirts
$11 each

BOOTS
10% off

Raincoats
25% off

1. What is the discount on a sweater that regularly costs $25?

   _____

2. What is the sale price of a raincoat that regularly costs $84?

   _____

3. What would be the cost of 2 pairs of jeans that regularly cost $30 each?

   _____

4. Brittany wants to buy a pair of boots that regularly cost $70 and a sweater that regularly costs $30. What is the total cost, excluding tax?

   _____

5. Carleen buys 2 T-shirts and a sweater that regularly costs $40. What is the total cost of her purchases, excluding tax?

   _____

Solve the pan-balance problems.

6.

   $4\triangle$ $3\square$ $9\square$

   One triangle weighs as much as _____ boxes.

7.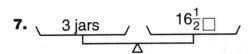

   3 jars $16\frac{1}{2}\square$

   One jar weighs as much as _____ boxes.

Practice Set 34 *continued*

Write your answers below or on another piece of paper.

Answer the questions about the figures below.

A   B   C   D

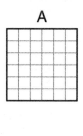 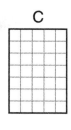 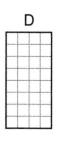

8. Which figure has an area of 36 square units and a perimeter of 24 units? _____

9. Which figure has the largest perimeter, and what is it? _____

10. Which two figures have the same area? _____

Write <, >, or = to make the number sentences true.

11. 11.8 _____ $\frac{1}{5} * 60$

12. $\frac{4}{6} * 48$ _____ 32% of 100

13. $\frac{8}{10}$ _____ $0.5 * 3$

14. 0.78 _____ $78 * 10^{-3}$

15. $6,586$ _____ $70 * 90$

16. $\frac{1}{2} * 0.5$ _____ $25 * 10^{-2}$

Solve.

17. $10^5 * 10^8 =$ _____

18. $10^{\square} = 10^6 * 10^{-3}$

19. $9.8 * 10^3 =$ _____

20. $90,000 = 9 * 10^{\square}$

21. $A = (3^3 * 26) / 2^3$

22. $1.3 * 10^5 / B = 2$

23. $C = (8.7 + 3.8) * 5$

24. $715 + (100 * 2.94) = D$

25. $7.2 * 10^4 =$ _____

26. $802 + (1,000 * 8.1) = F$

27. $6.3 * 10^5 =$ _____

28. $10^{\square} = 10^{-2} * 10^{-1}$

Practice Set 35

Use with or after
Lesson 5·1

Write your answers below or on another piece of paper.

Use your full-circle protractor to measure each angle.

1.

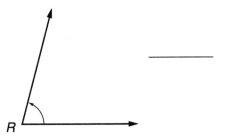

_____

2.

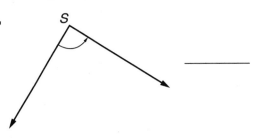

_____

Tell whether each angle appears to be *acute, right, obtuse, straight,* or *reflex.*

3.

_____

4.

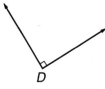

_____

5.

_____

6.

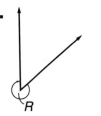

_____

7.

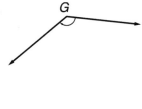

_____

8.

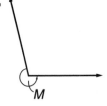

_____

Answer the following question.

9. If the long side is 6.9 cm and the short side is 2.4 cm, what is the perimeter?

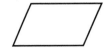

_____

Practice Set 35 *continued*

Use with or after
Lesson 5·1

Write your answers below or on another piece of paper.

10. Use the clues to complete the puzzle.

_____ _____ _____, _____ _____ _____, _____ _____ _____, _____ _____ _____

- Find 10% of 40. Double the result and write it in the thousands place.

- Subtract 6 from the number in the thousands place. Write the answer in the hundred-billions place.

- Find 16 * 3. Reverse the digits in the result and divide by 42. Write the result in the millions place.

- Add 5 to the digit in the hundred-billions place. Divide by 7 and write the result in the hundred-thousands place.

- Write $\frac{28}{7}$ as a whole number in the hundred-millions place.

- Find 35% of 20. Write the result in the ten-millions place.

- Subtract 1 from the number in the hundred-millions place. Write the result in the ten-billions place.

- Find $\frac{8}{9}$ of 108. Divide by 12 and write the result in the billions place.

- Find the sum of all the digits in the chart so far. Divide the result by 7 and write the answer in the hundreds place.

- Write 0 in the remaining places less than billions.

11. Write the number in words.

_____

Name _____ Date _____ Time _____

Practice Set 36

Use with or after
Lesson 5·2

SRB
75–77
163 233 260

Write your answers below or on another piece of paper.

Write the measure of each angle. Do not use a protractor.

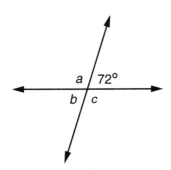

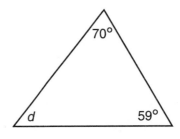

1. m∠a = _____

2. m∠b = _____

3. m∠c = _____

4. m∠d = _____

Solve.

5.   13
   $*$ 18

6.   28,681
   $+$ 9,478

7. $78\overline{)3,734}$

8. A school ordered 145 math books. The books were shipped in boxes that held 8 books each. How many boxes did the school receive?

_____

Write the numbers in order from least to greatest.

9. 3.48, $3\frac{4}{8}$,   4.8,   3.75, $4\frac{2}{5}$,   4.41

_____, _____, _____, _____, _____, _____

10. $4\frac{1}{2}$,   4.75,   2, $3\frac{1}{4}$,   4.8, $4\frac{7}{8}$

_____, _____, _____, _____, _____, _____

11. 0.10, $\frac{1}{1,000}$,   0.01,   1.11, $1\frac{1}{10}$,   1.01

_____, _____, _____, _____, _____, _____

12. 8.3, $9\frac{1}{6}$, $8\frac{1}{3}$,   11.01, $9\frac{7}{16}$,   10.8, $10\frac{4}{6}$, $11\frac{1}{5}$

_____, _____, _____, _____, _____, _____, _____, _____

13. $7\frac{5}{8}$,   7.08,   7.88, $7\frac{3}{4}$,   7.8, $7\frac{1}{2}$

_____, _____, _____, _____, _____, _____

14. 6.0, $5\frac{1}{3}$, $6\frac{3}{10}$, $4\frac{1}{5}$,   6.03,   5.33

_____, _____, _____, _____, _____, _____

Practice Set 37

Use with or after
Lesson 5·3

Write your answers below or on another piece of paper.

Find the number of degrees in a sector of a circle graph to show each percent.

1. 15% _____

2. 30% _____

3. 50% _____

4. 5% _____

5. 10% _____

6. 75% _____

Miranda surveyed her classmates about their favorite beverage. She recorded her results in the tally table below.

7. Draw a circle graph to show her results.

Favorite Beverage	
Beverage	**Number of Students**
Milk	ЖЖ ЖЖ ЖЖ ///
Chocolate milk	///
Orange juice	ЖЖ /
Apple juice	//
Soda	ЖЖ //

8. Elliot made 3 of 8 shots in the basketball game. What fraction of the shots did he make?

_____

9. What percent of the shots did he miss?

_____

10. At this rate, how many shots would he make if he took 24 shots?

_____

11. Jack has drawn a diagram of shelves he plans to make. Each board is $\frac{7}{8}$ inch thick. What is the width of the shelves?

_____

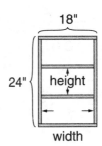

12. If the boards are all equally spaced, what is the height of each shelf?

_____

Practice Set 38

Write your answers below or on another piece of paper.

Plot and label the following points.

> **Example** A (3,2)
> The point is plotted on the grid.

1. B (0,4)

2. C (−1,5)

3. D (−2,−4)

4. E (0,0)

5. F (5,1)

6. G (2,−1)

7. H (3,−3)

8. I (−3,3)

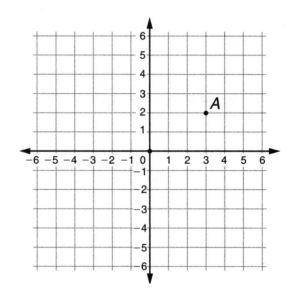

Write the lowest common denominator for each pair of fractions.

9. $\frac{2}{3}, \frac{1}{4}$ _____

10. $\frac{11}{15}, \frac{2}{5}$ _____

11. $\frac{3}{5}, \frac{1}{2}$ _____

12. $\frac{5}{8}, \frac{7}{12}$ _____

13. $\frac{5}{6}, \frac{7}{12}$ _____

14. $\frac{3}{8}, \frac{3}{14}$ _____

Insert parentheses to make each sentence true.

15. $100 - 40 \div 10 = 6$

16. $35 - 3 / 2 + 2 = 8$

17. $5 * 6 + 100 / 5 = 50$

18. $27 * 2 - 4 / 2 = 25$

Practice Set 38 continued

Write your answers below or on another piece of paper.

Find the distance from 0 to each point and then answer the questions below.

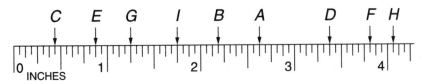

19. A _____

20. B _____

21. C _____

22. D _____

23. E _____

24. F _____

25. G _____

26. H _____

27. I _____

28. What is the distance between points A and I? _____

29. What is the distance between points C and H? _____

30. What is the distance between points B and G? _____

---

31. Complete the table.

Product	Exponential Notation	Standard Notation
12 * 12 * 12 * 12 * 12 * 12		
	$6^{\square}$	7,776
	$\square^{8}$	6,561
	10^{-11}	
19 * 19 * 19		

Find the percent of the following.

32. 25% of 280 _____

33. 20% of 70 _____

34. 30% of 0.4 _____

35. 42% of 250 _____

36. 3% of 18 _____

37. 76% of 10 _____

38. 11% of 900 _____

39. 77% of 800 _____

40. 34% of 450 _____

41. 1% of 76 _____

42. 10% of 1.3 _____

43. 0.1% of 121 _____

Practice Set 39

Write your answers below or on another piece of paper.

Match the letter of the figure that is congruent with the one given.

1. _____

A.

2. _____

B.

3. _____

C.

4. _____

D.

5. _____

E.

Write an algebraic expression for each word, expression, or situation.

6. 5 more than c _____

7. h divided by 2 _____

8. 10 times d _____

9. m subtracted from 1,050 _____

10. Ellen has twice as many tea cups in her collection as Sara. If Sara has t tea cups, how many does Ellen have?

_____

11. Stephan is s meters tall. His brother Eric is 0.2 meters taller. How tall is Eric?

_____

Practice Set 39 *continued*

Use with or after
Lesson 5·6

Write your answers below or on another piece of paper.

Solve.

12. 28)$\overline{448}$ **13.** 12)$\overline{780}$ **14.** 14)$\overline{4,690}$ **15.** 278)$\overline{1,112}$

16. $\begin{array}{r} 634 \\ -\ 456 \end{array}$ **17.** $\begin{array}{r} (-33) \\ +\ 735 \end{array}$ **18.** $\begin{array}{r} 346 \\ +\ 86 \end{array}$ **19.** $\begin{array}{r} 512 \\ *\ 27 \end{array}$

20. 5)$\overline{1,185}$ **21.** $\begin{array}{r} 40.97 \\ -\ 16.82 \end{array}$ **22.** $\begin{array}{r} 4.4 \\ -\ 3.9 \end{array}$ **23.** $\begin{array}{r} 7.1 \\ *\ 6.3 \end{array}$

24. $\begin{array}{r} 95.235 \\ -\ 37.023 \end{array}$ **25.** 4)$\overline{7.45}$ **26.** $\begin{array}{r} 853 \\ -\ 563 \end{array}$ **27.** $\begin{array}{r} 6,384 \\ +\ 364 \end{array}$

28. $\begin{array}{r} 465,891,000 \\ -\ 312,747,000 \end{array}$ **29.** $\begin{array}{r} 72.94 \\ +\ 13.97 \end{array}$ **30.** $\begin{array}{r} 6.7 \\ *\ 8.1 \end{array}$

Suppose you spin the base of the spinner 1,440 times.

31. How many times would you

expect it to land on Part A? _____

32. How many times would you

expect it to land on Part B? _____

33. How many times would you

expect it to land on Part C? _____

34. How many times would you

expect it NOT to land on Part B? _____

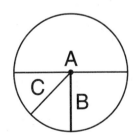

Practice Set 40

Use with or after
Lesson 5·9

Write your answers below or on another piece of paper.

Find the measure of each angle without using a protractor.

1. m∠a = _____

2. m∠b = _____

3. m∠c = _____

4. m∠d = _____

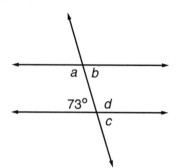

Find the greatest common factor for each pair of numbers.

5. 6, 9 _____

6. 4, 20 _____

7. 9, 10 _____

8. 16, 24 _____

9. 9, 12 _____

10. 8, 18 _____

Write the coordinates for each point.

Example   R (3,–2)

11. J _____

12. K _____

13. L _____

14. M _____

15. N _____

16. O _____

17. P _____

18. Q _____

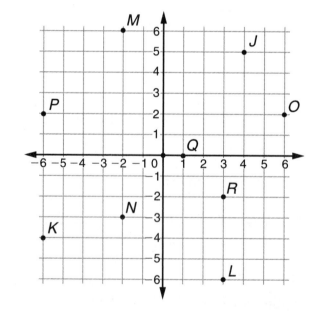

Practice Set 41

Use with or after
Lesson 5·10

SRB
109 140
212 233

Write your answers below or on another piece of paper.

Figure *LMNP* is a parallelogram. Find the measure of each angle without using a protractor.

1. m∠*r* = _____

2. m∠*s* = _____

3. m∠*t* = _____

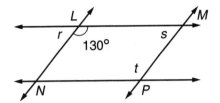

The figure *EFGH* is a rectangle.

4. What is the measure of ∠*E*? _____

5. What is the length of $\overline{EF}$? _____

6. What is the length of $\overline{FG}$? _____

7. What is the perimeter of rectangle *EFGH*? _____

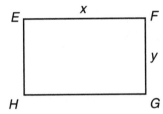

Use the graph to answer the questions below.

At a marathon, Ariana runs at a pace of 6 miles per hour. Glenn walks at a brisk pace that is slightly slower than Ariana's speed.

8. What is Glenn's walking pace?

_____

9. After 3 hours, how much farther has Ariana gone?

_____

10. How much longer will it take Glenn to walk 24 miles than Ariana to run 24 miles?

_____

11. How far behind Ariana is Glenn after 7 hours?

_____

12. Do you think this graph is realistic? Why or why not?

_____

_____

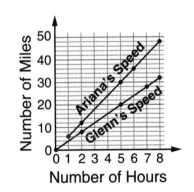

Practice Set 41 *continued*

Use with or after Lesson 5·10

Write your answers below or on another piece of paper.

Answer the following:

13. What is the name of the polygon?

_____

14. If the perimeter is 4.48 cm, what is the length of each side?

_____

Write each in standard notation.

15. fourteen and four-fifths _____

16. seven hundred eighty-eight trillion, three hundred billion, forty-three million

_____

17. thirty-seven and four hundred eighty-nine thousandths

_____

18. sixteen trillion, two hundred sixty billion, five hundred million

_____

Write the words for the following numbers:

19. 5,798,232,026,590 _____

20. 684.948 _____

21. $23\frac{7}{8}$ _____

22. 55.927 _____

Write each fraction as a decimal and a percent.

23.

Fraction	$\frac{4}{5}$	$\frac{5}{9}$	$\frac{2}{5}$	$\frac{7}{10}$	$\frac{30}{42}$	$\frac{7}{12}$	$5\frac{1}{16}$
Decimal							
Percent							

24.

Fraction	$6\frac{3}{4}$	$2\frac{1}{8}$	$\frac{9}{10}$	$\frac{1}{2}$	$\frac{19}{20}$	$4\frac{1}{4}$	$16\frac{3}{5}$
Decimal							
Percent							

Practice Set 42

Use with or after
Lesson 6·1

Write your answers below or on another piece of paper.

Find the reciprocal of each number.

1. $\frac{4}{5}$ _____

2. $\frac{7}{12}$ _____

3. 5 _____

4. $\frac{3}{7}$ _____

5. $1\frac{1}{2}$ _____

6. 9 _____

7. $4\frac{2}{3}$ _____

8. $7\frac{3}{5}$ _____

Multiply. Write your answers in simplest form.

9. $5 * \frac{1}{5} =$ _____

10. $6 * \frac{2}{3} =$ _____

11. $\frac{3}{7} * \frac{2}{5} =$ _____

12. $1\frac{1}{2} * 5 =$ _____

13. $2\frac{1}{8} * 5\frac{1}{3} =$ _____

14. $4\frac{1}{5} * \frac{5}{7} =$ _____

Divide. Round to the nearest hundredth.

15. 543 / 9 _____

16. 265 / 6 _____

17. 921 / 7 _____

18. 497 / 3 _____

19. 251 / 12 _____

20. 801 / 27 _____

Use digits to write the following numbers:

21. eighty-two billion, six hundred thirty-three million

_____

22. seventy-two million, one hundred sixteen thousand, four hundred forty-nine

_____

23. seven and eight-tenths

_____

24. twelve and ninety-three hundredths

_____

Practice Set 42 *continued*

Write your answers below or on another piece of paper.

25. Write the missing numbers for the table.

Fraction	Percent	Decimal
$\frac{7}{8}$		
		0.99
	38%	
		2.03

Solve.

Christie bought two pairs of sandals that were $12.99 each. Adam bought three pairs of sandals. His total came to $24.57.

26. Who paid more money overall? _____

27. Who got the better deal per pair of shoes? Explain. _____

John bought a tool set that was 25% off. The original price was $48.

28. How much did he pay for the tool set? _____

29. How much money did John save? _____

30 LeAnn paid $\frac{1}{4}$ of the price that Richard paid for 10 pencils. LeAnn paid $2 for the pencils. How much did Richard pay for one pencil?

_____

---

31. Use the digits to write the largest number less than 5.

6, 4, 2, 0, 9

_____ _____ , _____ _____ _____

Practice Set 43

Write your answers below or on another piece of paper.

Divide. Show your work. Write each answer in simplest form.

Example $\frac{4}{5} \div \frac{3}{10}$
$\frac{4}{5} * \frac{10}{3} = \frac{40}{8}$
Answer: 5

1. $\frac{1}{3} \div \frac{1}{2}$

Answer: _____

2. $\frac{3}{5} \div \frac{3}{10}$

Answer: _____

3. $\frac{7}{8} \div \frac{4}{5}$

Answer: _____

4. $\frac{4}{9} \div \frac{4}{9}$

Answer: _____

5. $6 \div \frac{1}{5}$

Answer: _____

6. $\frac{1}{2} \div \frac{3}{8}$

Answer: _____

7. $2\frac{1}{5} \div \frac{1}{10}$

Answer: _____

8. $9 \div \frac{1}{3}$

Answer: _____

9. $3\frac{1}{2} \div \frac{1}{12}$

Answer: _____

10. $5\frac{1}{3} \div \frac{8}{5}$

Answer: _____

11. $3 \div \frac{3}{8}$

Answer: _____

12. $4\frac{1}{6} \div \frac{5}{8}$

Answer: _____

13. $\frac{2}{5} \div \frac{1}{2}$

Answer: _____

14. $4\frac{3}{8} \div \frac{2}{7}$

Answer: _____

Solve.

15. $\begin{array}{r} 2,247 \\ -\ 1,894 \\ \hline \end{array}$

16. $\begin{array}{r} 1,309 \\ +\ 782 \\ \hline \end{array}$

17. $\begin{array}{r} 837 \\ -\ 784 \\ \hline \end{array}$

18. $18\overline{)556}$

19. $\begin{array}{r} 8,926 \\ -\ 2,481 \\ \hline \end{array}$

20. $\begin{array}{r} 41 \\ *\ 83 \\ \hline \end{array}$

21. $37\overline{)6,298}$

22. $\begin{array}{r} 6,473 \\ -\ 5,498 \\ \hline \end{array}$

23. $\begin{array}{r} 723 \\ *\ 3 \\ \hline \end{array}$

24. $\begin{array}{r} 31,955 \\ +\ 19,079 \\ \hline \end{array}$

25. $\begin{array}{r} 904 \\ *\ 61 \\ \hline \end{array}$

26. $\begin{array}{r} 16,980 \\ +\ 14,062 \\ \hline \end{array}$

Practice Set 43 *continued*

Use with or after
Lesson 6·2

SRB
234 240
253

Write your answers below or on another piece of paper.

Complete each pattern. Then describe the pattern.

27. 12, 19, 26, _____, 40, _____, _____, 61

_____

28. 142, 71, 35.5, _____, 8.875, _____, 2.21875

_____

29. 0, 4, _____, 5, _____, 6, 0, _____, 0, 8

_____

30. _____, 0, 1.4, _____, _____, 5.6, _____, 8.4

_____

Plot the points shown and write each letter next to the given ordered pair.
Connect the points in alphabetical order.

31 *A:* (−1,−9)   **32.** *G:* (0,−3)

33. *M:* (6,7)   **34.** *O:* (2,5)

35. *D:* (3,−1)   **36.** *B:* (−1,−6)

37. *U:* (−5,3)   **38.** *K:* (3,1)

39. *L:* (4,4)   **40.** *N:* (3,6)

41. *C:* (2,−4)   **42.** *T:* (−5,5)

43. *J:* (−1,0)   **44.** *V:* (−3,1)

45. *Q:* (−2,5)   **46.** *E:* (4,1)

47. *F:* (2,−1)   **48.** *S:* (−6,7)

49. *I:* (−1,−2)   **50.** *P:* (0,7)

51. *R:* (−3,6)   **52.** *H:* (−1,−4)

53. *W:* (−1,0)

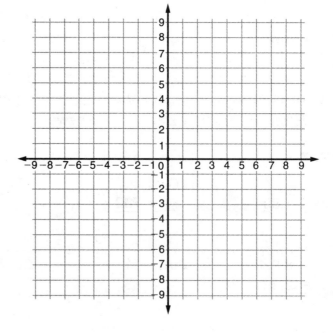

Practice Set 44

Use with or after
Lesson 6·3

Write your answers below or on another piece of paper.

Subtract.

1. $16 - (-14) =$ _____

2. $-125 - 87 =$ _____

3. $3.5 - (-6.7) =$ _____

4. $-5.7 - (-8.9) =$ _____

5. $-4\frac{1}{2} - (-6\frac{1}{2}) =$ _____

6. $12.83 - (-6.59) =$ _____

7. $257 - (-183) =$ _____

8. $5 - (-4\frac{2}{3}) =$ _____

9. $15.8 - (-3.3) =$ _____

10. $3\frac{5}{16} - (-1\frac{5}{8}) =$ _____

Write the numbers in exponential notation.

11. $10 * 10 * 10 =$ _____

12. $14 * 14 * 14 * 14 * 14 =$ _____

13. $2 * 2 =$ _____

14. $7 * 7 * 7 * 7 =$ _____

15. $143 * 143 * 143 * 143 * 143 * 143 * 143 =$ _____

16. $10{,}416 * 10{,}416 * 10{,}416 =$ _____

Add or subtract. Write all answers greater than 1 as mixed numbers. Write all answers in simplest form.

17. $\frac{2}{7} + \frac{1}{4} =$ _____

18. $\frac{4}{9} + \frac{2}{3} =$ _____

19. $\frac{1}{2} - \frac{14}{30} =$ _____

20. $\frac{6}{7} - \frac{1}{14} =$ _____

21. $\frac{9}{4} + \frac{1}{6} =$ _____

22. $\frac{5}{6} - \frac{2}{3} =$ _____

23. $\frac{1}{24} + \frac{2}{3} =$ _____

24. $\frac{15}{16} + \frac{3}{4} =$ _____

25. $\frac{9}{10} - \frac{2}{5} =$ _____

26. $\frac{11}{36} + \frac{1}{2} =$ _____

27. $\frac{7}{12} - \frac{1}{2} =$ _____

28. $\frac{17}{20} - \frac{4}{5} =$ _____

29. $\frac{13}{18} + \frac{1}{9} =$ _____

30. $\frac{3}{5} + \frac{1}{10} =$ _____

31. $\frac{8}{9} - \frac{1}{3} =$ _____

Practice Set 45

Use with or after
Lesson 6·4

Write your answers below or on another piece of paper.

Solve.

1. $-7 * -5 =$ _____

2. $56 / (-8) =$ _____

3. $(-180) / 10 =$ _____

4. $(-9) * 6 =$ _____

5. $(-63) \div (-9) =$ _____

6. $(-3) * 4 * (-8) =$ _____

7. $(23 - 3) / (-5) =$ _____

8. $60 / (-5) =$ _____

9. $(-6) * (8 + 5) =$ _____

10. $(-2 - 12) / 2 =$ _____

Evaluate each algebraic expression for $a = 5$ and $f = 1.2$.

11. $6 * a$

12. $9 - f$

13. $30 / a$

14. $7 + f$

15. $50 - a$

16. $10f$

17. $2(f + 0.8)$

18. $a / 5$

19. $8 + 2a$

Write an algebraic expression for each phrase.

20. A number t increased by 35 _____

21. The sum of a number m and 105 _____

22. A number s decreased by 19 _____

23. The total when a number s is added to 31 _____

24. 50 decreased by a number x _____

25. A number r minus 7 _____

Practice Set 45 *continued*

Use with or after
Lesson 6·4

Write your answers below or on another piece of paper.

Complete the following tables.

26.

Rule
out = in / 6

in	out
42	
36	
6	
0	
1	

27.

Rule
out = in $* \frac{1}{2}$

in	out
7	
4	
2	
0	
$\frac{1}{2}$	

28.

Rule
out = in $*$ 0.01

in	out
17	
101	
42	
16	
33	

29.

Rule
out = in $*$ 13

in	out
8	
0	
19	
21	
65	

30.

Rule
out = in + 1.4

in	out
3.7	
4.2	
8.1	
0.2	
19.04	

31.

Rule
out = in − 27

in	out
36	
81	
90	
74	
60	

Find the mean for the following groups of numbers.

32. 4, 9, 8, 7, 1, 0, 9

Mean = _____

33. 14, 19, 24, 16, 31, 29, 18

Mean = _____

Practice Set 46

Write your answers below or on another piece of paper.

Match each number sentence with a property. Write the letter of the number sentence.

1. Distributive Property
of Multiplication
over Addition _____

A. 7(6.2 − 5.1) = 7(6.2) − 7(5.1)

2. Commutative Property
of Addition _____

B. $\frac{1}{3}(9 + 5) = \frac{1}{3}(9) + \frac{1}{3}(5)$

3. Associative Property
of Multiplication _____

C. (15 − 6) + 8 = 8 + (15 − 6)

4. Commutative Property
of Multiplication _____

D. 3 * 1 = 3

5. Distributive Property
of Multiplication
over Subtraction _____

E. 3 * (2 * 5) = (3 * 2) * 5

6. Identity Property
for Multiplication _____

F. 25 * 150 = 150 * 25

Compare. Write < , >, or =.

7. −24 + (−5) _____ 162 −70

8. −5 − 4 _____ 0

9. −100 − 43 _____ −200 + 57

10. 9.2 − (−6.1) _____ 8.2 + 4.5

11. −153 _____ (−6) * (−8) * (−3)

12. 425 * 0 _____ −260 + 260

13. (−5) * (−6) _____ (4.6) * (−3.1)

14. −529 + 60 _____ −500 − 37

Practice Set 47

Use with or after
Lesson 6·6

Write your answers below or on another piece of paper.

Evaluate each expression.

1. $17 + 3 * 2 - 1$ _____

2. $3^2 + 7(10 - 5)$ _____

3. $(5.1 + 9.4) * 3 + 2$ _____

4. $(4 + 16) / 10 + 9$ _____

5. $100 - 62 * 3 + 75$ _____

6. $\frac{3}{5} * \frac{1}{3} + \frac{1}{10} * 2$ _____

7. Use the clues to complete the place-value puzzle.

_____ . _____ _____ _____ _____   .

- Write 75% of 12 in the hundredths place.
- Find $\frac{1}{25}$ of 115. Add 1.4 and write the result in the thousandths place.
- Take $\frac{4}{9}$ of the number in the hundredths place. Write the result in the ten-thousandths place.
- Multiply $8 * 34$. Subtract 265 and write the result in the ones place.
- Subtract 200% of 0.5 from the number in the thousandths place. Write the result in the tenths place.

Solve.

8.   736
       + 264

9.   253
       + 86

10.   365
        − 375

11.   253
        − 27

12.   364
        − 94

13.   7,437
        + 983

14.   6,345
        + 1,052

15.   2,852
        − 1,865

Practice Set 47 *continued*

Use with or after
Lesson 6·6

Write your answers below or on another piece of paper.

Convert each fraction into a whole number or mixed number.

16. $\frac{14}{3}$ _____   **17.** $\frac{9}{1}$ _____   **18.** $\frac{23}{8}$ _____   **19.** $\frac{10}{2}$ _____

20. $\frac{18}{5}$ _____   **21.** $\frac{26}{6}$ _____   **22.** $\frac{30}{4}$ _____   **23.** $\frac{25}{7}$ _____

24. $\frac{20}{10}$ _____   **25.** $\frac{27}{3}$ _____   **26.** $\frac{98}{5}$ _____   **27.** $\frac{19}{4}$ _____

Answer each question. You can use the number line to help you.

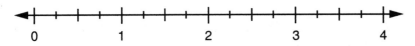

28. What is $\frac{1}{4}$ of 4? _____   **29.** What is $\frac{1}{2}$ of $\frac{1}{2}$? _____

30. What is $\frac{1}{2}$ of $\frac{1}{4}$? _____   **31.** What is $\frac{1}{4}$ of 1? _____

32. What is $\frac{1}{2}$ of 3? _____   **33.** What is $\frac{1}{8}$ of 2? _____

34. What is $\frac{3}{4}$ of 4? _____   **35.** What is $\frac{5}{8}$ of 2? _____

36. What is $\frac{3}{8}$ of 4? _____   **37.** What is $\frac{3}{4}$ of 3? _____

38. What is $\frac{2}{3}$ of 3? _____   **39.** What is $\frac{1}{2}$ of $\frac{3}{4}$? _____

Order the fractions from least to greatest.

40. $\frac{1}{6}, \frac{1}{9}, \frac{1}{12}, \frac{1}{15}$ _____, _____, _____, _____

41. $\frac{2}{7}, \frac{4}{13}, \frac{5}{6}, \frac{6}{13}$ _____, _____, _____, _____

42. $\frac{2}{3}, \frac{1}{6}, \frac{3}{4}, \frac{11}{12}$ _____, _____, _____, _____

43. $\frac{7}{12}, \frac{1}{4}, \frac{7}{8}, \frac{5}{6}$ _____, _____, _____, _____

44. $\frac{3}{16}, \frac{1}{8}, \frac{3}{4}, \frac{1}{2}$ _____, _____, _____, _____

45. $\frac{4}{5}, \frac{3}{10}, \frac{1}{2}, \frac{1}{15}$ _____, _____, _____, _____

Practice Set 48

Use with or after Lesson 6·7

Write your answers below or on another piece of paper.

Write *true* or *false* for each number sentence.

1. 9 * 8 = 72 _____

2. 100 − 36 = 65 _____

3. 6 * 4 − 3 = 6 _____

4. 126 / 7 = 20 _____

5. 125 − 150 / 50 = 122 _____

6. 90 − 45 ≤ 45 _____

7. 80 / (4 + 4) ≥ 12 _____

8. 12 * 12 ≠ 135 _____

9. 40 + (6 * 2) = 48 _____

10. 92 / 6 + 7 < 50 _____

Write the letter of the line plot that makes sense with the survey question.

```
        X                          X
        X                          X
    X   X   X                      X
    X   X   X                      X   X
    X   X   X              X    X   X   X   X
    X   X   X   X          X    X   X   X   X
X   X   X   X   X          X    X   X   X   X
_____        _____
6   7   8   9   10          0   1   2   3   4
```

Line Plot A   **Line Plot B**

11. How many hours do you sleep each night? _____

12. How many hours of TV do you watch each day? _____

Add. Use mental math.

13. (−1) + 2 + (−11) = _____

14. (−17) + (8) = _____

15. (−5) + 6 + (−1) = _____

16. 10 + (−3) + 2 = _____

17. 3 + (−5) + (−6) = _____

18. −9 + (−4) + 2 = _____

Practice Set 49

Write your answers below or on another piece of paper.

Find the solution to each equation.

1. 4 + a = 10

2. 20 + t = 50

3. 18 = b + 9

4. $\frac{1}{3} * p = \frac{4}{15}$

5. 25c = 200

6. 4n = 60

Estimate. Round to the nearest whole number, the nearest ten, or the nearest hundred before you multiply.

7. 762 * 81 _____

8. 2.4 * 6.7 _____

9. 91 * 823 _____

10. 52.1 * 76.3 _____

11. 801 * 104 _____

12. 4.72 * 1.07 _____

13. 484 * 621 _____

14. 4.72 * 5.07 _____

15. 708 * 814 _____

16. 312 * 847 _____

17. 907 * 382 _____

18. 6.09 * 1.49 _____

19. 3.2002 * 3.2002 _____

20. 8.01 * 1.24967 _____

21. 3.132 * 9.17 _____

22. 1.00769 * 712.514 _____

23. 6.26 * 7.39 _____

24. 1618 * 1732 _____

Divide. Include remainders in your answers where needed.

25. 2,158 ÷ 83 = _____

26. 1,633 ÷ 71 = _____

27. 42,240 ÷ 352 = _____

28. 366,450 ÷ 698 = _____

29. 206,322 ÷ 411 = _____

30. 576,312 ÷ 814 = _____

31. 251 ÷ 21 → _____

32. 1,410 ÷ 13 → _____

33. 7,621 ÷ 63 → _____

34. 904 ÷ 204 → _____

Practice Set 50

Write your answers below or on another piece of paper.

Solve each pan-balance problem. In each drawing, the two pans are in perfect balance.

1. One cube weighs as much as _____ marbles.

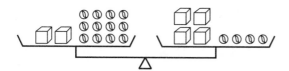

2. One baseball bat weighs as much as _____ balls.

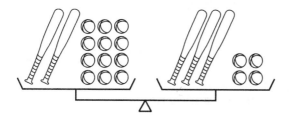

3. One P weighs as much as _____ Q.

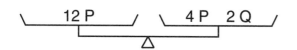

4. One B weighs as much as _____ G.

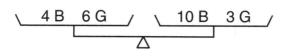

5. One T weighs as much as _____ S.

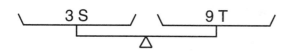

6. One L weighs as much as _____ A.

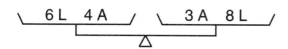

Practice Set 50 *continued*

Write your answers below or on another piece of paper.

Use the grid to answer the questions below.

Each square in the grid below represents a city block. There are 8 blocks in a mile, so each side of each block is $\frac{1}{8}$ mile long.

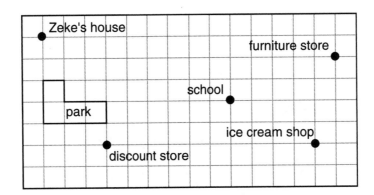

7. What is the shortest distance between Zeke's house and school?

_____

8. If Zeke goes to the ice cream shop before going home from school, how far will he have walked?

_____

9. After leaving the house, Zeke's mom dropped Zeke and his brother at the park, then drove to the discount store and the furniture store before returning home. What is the shortest distance she could have driven?

_____

10. What is the area of the park, in square miles?

_____

11. What is the area, in square miles, shown on the entire grid map?

_____

Practice Set 51

Use with or after
Lesson 6·11

Write your answers below or on another piece of paper.

Evaluate each algebraic expression.

1. $3y - 4 = 11$

2. $10 = 2n$

3. $12 = 14 - z$

4. $16 + 7 = m$

5. $16 = p^4$

6. $21 = 7s - 7$

7. $17 * r / 2 = 34$

8. $104 \div q = 13$

9. $7 = 49 / a$

10. $(s \div 3) + 12 = 12$

11. $6 = \frac{36}{b} + 2$

12. $8u - 4 = 44$

13. $8 + 7w = 15$

14. $0 = (104 + 206) * d$

15. $9^2 = x$

16. $\frac{6h}{2} = 27$

17. $44 = 3x + 8$

18. $\frac{96}{y} = 24$

Solve.

19. 8.47
      $* 6$

20. 3.19
      $* 100$

21. 4.45
      $+ 6.96$

22. 2.408
      $+ 7.334$

23. 9.294
      $- 6.275$

24. 7.025
      $* 8$

25. 12,645
      $- 6,792$

26. 33.25
      $+ 79.87$

27. $\frac{1}{4} + \frac{3}{4} + \frac{5}{6} =$ _____

28. $14.812 + 12.265 + 6.408 =$ _____

29. $\frac{2}{3} * \frac{7}{9} =$ _____

30. $5 - (\frac{4}{5} + \frac{2}{3}) =$ _____

Practice Set 52

Write your answers below or on another piece of paper.

Match the solution set with the inequality. Write the letter of the solution set.

1. $5 < r$ _____

2. $-\frac{15}{3} \geq s$ _____

3. $4s > 24$ _____

4. $9y \leq 18$ _____

5. $25 - 4 > p$ _____

A. All numbers less than 21

B. All numbers less than or equal to -5

C. All numbers less than or equal to 2

D. All numbers greater than 6

E. All numbers greater than 5

Find the least common multiple for each pair of numbers.

6. 9, 20 _____

7. 30, 36 _____

8. 7, 10 _____

9. 5, 10 _____

10. 12, 16 _____

11. 7, 8 _____

Add parentheses to the number sentences to make them correct.

12. $24 - 15 + 7 = 16$

13. $24 - 15 + 7 = 2$

14. $15 + 15 * 4 = 75$

15. $15 + 15 * 4 = 120$

16. $21 - 12 / 3 * 2 = 13$

17. $21 - 12 / 3 * 2 = 34$

18. $17 - 9 + 4 + 3 = 15$

19. $17 - 9 + 4 + 3 = 1$

20. $45 / 9 + 6 = 3$

21. $45 / 9 + 6 = 11$

Complete.

22. $\frac{1}{3}$ hr $= \frac{\quad}{15}$ hr

23. $\frac{1}{2}$ min $= \frac{4}{\quad}$ min

24. $\frac{2}{6}$ hr $= \frac{\quad}{3}$ hr

25. $\frac{\quad}{8}$ hr $= \frac{12}{32}$ hr

Practice Set 52 *continued*

Use with or after
Lesson 6·12

SRB
136–137
241

Write your answers below or on another piece of paper.

The town of State College lies in a valley that experiences much precipitation. Use the data in the tables for questions 26–29.

Average Number of Days in State College with at Least 0.01 Inch of Precipitation

Month	Jan.	Feb.	Mar.	Apr.	May	June
Number of Days	18	17	15	14	10	8

Month	July	Aug.	Sept.	Oct.	Nov.	Dec.
Number of Days	9	11	17	20	20	18

26. Use the information about precipitation in State College to make a broken-line graph.

27. Find the mean for the number of days with at least 0.01 inch of precipitation.

_____

28. Find the mode for the number of days State College received at least 0.01 inch of precipitation.

_____

29. Find the median for the graph.

_____

Write *true* or *false* for each number sentence.

30. $(9+3) / 4 = 3$ _____

31. $\frac{9}{(3+6)} = 9$ _____

32. $6 - (2 / 4) = 5\frac{1}{2}$ _____

33. $18 + (9 * 4) = 54$ _____

34. $(8 + 7) = 8 + 7$ _____

35. $(6 * 4) - 2 = 20$ _____

36. $6 + \frac{1}{8} = \frac{(6 + 1)}{8}$ _____

37. $4^2 = 2^2 * 4$ _____

38. $4^2 > 2^5$ _____

39. $\frac{(2 + 4)}{3} = 2 + \frac{4}{3}$ _____

40. $(3 + 2) * 12 = 60$ _____

41. $\left(\frac{6}{3}\right) + \left(\frac{8}{3}\right) = \frac{(6 + 8)}{3}$ _____

Practice Set 53

Write your answers below or on another piece of paper.

Use the spinners to help you answer questions 1–4.

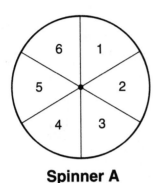

Spinner A

Spinner B

1. Which spinner has outcomes that are equally likely? _____

2. What is the probability of spinning an even number using Spinner A? _____

3. What is the probability of spinning an odd number using Spinner B? _____

4. What is the probability of spinning a number less than 5 using Spinner A? _____

Find the measure of the missing angles without measuring.

5.

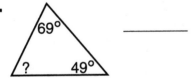

_____

6.

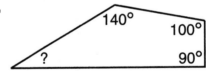

_____

Write < or >.

7. 9.4 _____ $\frac{2}{5} * 20$

8. $\frac{7}{8} * 48$ _____ 34% of 150

9. $\frac{7}{10}$ _____ $\frac{4}{5} * \frac{1}{2}$

10. 0.04 _____ $4 * 10^{-1}$

11. 8.39 _____ $34 * \frac{1}{4}$

12. 7.31 _____ $73.1 * 10^{-1}$

Practice Set 54

Use with or after
Lesson 7·3

Write your answers below or on another piece of paper.

Use this section of a table of random digits to answer questions 1–4.

Let each digit represent the results of a game. Even stands for a win. Odd stands for a loss.

```
0 8 1 0 5 5 9 9 8 7
8 7 1 1 2 2 1 4 7 6
1 4 7 1 3 7 1 1 8 1
```

1. a. How many wins are in the first 10 games? _____

 b. What percent of the first 10 games are wins? _____

2. a. How many wins are in 20 games? _____

 b. What percent of the 20 games are wins? _____

3. a. How many wins are in 30 games? _____

 b. What percent of the 30 games are wins? _____

4. What do you think the percent of wins would be if you had a table of random digits that had 1,000 digits? Explain your answer.

_____

_____

Add parentheses to the number sentences to make them correct.

5. $143 = 7 + 6 * 11$

6. $7 + 6 * 11 = 73$

7. $54 - 22 + 17 = 49$

8. $15 = 54 - 22 + 17$

9. $46 = 7 * 4 + 18$

10. $7 * 4 + 18 = 154$

11. $6 * 2 + 19 * 7 = 145$

12. $6 * 2 + 19 * 7 = 882$

Solve.

13. $(-98) + (-25) = y$

14. $(+2,355) + (-5,234) = J$

15. $r + (+235) = (-945)$

16. $M = (-734) + (-900)$

85

Practice Set 55

Write your answers below or on another piece of paper.

Use the tree diagrams below to help you solve the problems.

1. Suppose 90 people walked through the maze below.

How many people would you expect to end up in Room A? _____

How many people would you expect to end up in Room B? _____

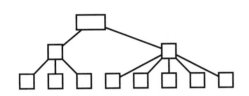
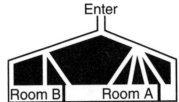

2. Suppose 120 people walked through the maze below.

How many people would you expect to end up in Room A? _____

How many people would you expect to end up in Room B? _____

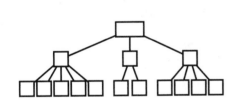
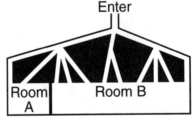

3. Suppose 100 people walked through the maze below.

How many people would you expect to end up in Room A? _____

How many people would you expect to end up in Room B? _____

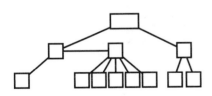
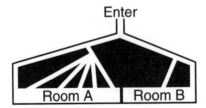

Practice Set 55 *continued*

Use with or after
Lesson 7·4

Write your answers below or on another piece of paper.

Multiply.

4. $\frac{4}{9} * \frac{1}{6} =$ _____

5. $\frac{2}{18} * \frac{16}{13} =$ _____

6. $\frac{7}{9} * \frac{12}{14} =$ _____

7. $\frac{8}{20} * \frac{7}{16} =$ _____

8. $\frac{7}{16} * \frac{9}{10} =$ _____

9. $\frac{3}{40} * \frac{2}{50} =$ _____

10. $\frac{14}{20} * \frac{7}{18} =$ _____

11. $\frac{46}{12} * \frac{11}{18} =$ _____

12. $\frac{12}{17} * \frac{21}{12} =$ _____

13. $\frac{4}{19} * \frac{3}{8} =$ _____

14. $\frac{2}{13} * \frac{24}{25} =$ _____

15. $\frac{0}{1} * \frac{82}{1000} =$ _____

16. $4\frac{1}{8} * 3\frac{1}{9} =$ _____

17. $1\frac{4}{6} * 3\frac{2}{9} =$ _____

18. $10\frac{3}{5} * 8\frac{7}{15} =$ _____

19. $9\frac{10}{17} * 4\frac{3}{9} =$ _____

20. $3\frac{1}{2} * 5\frac{1}{3} =$ _____

21. $21\frac{7}{8} * 1\frac{6}{7} =$ _____

22. $8\frac{9}{10} * 7\frac{9}{10} =$ _____

23. $6\frac{2}{3} * 6\frac{2}{3} =$ _____

24. $12\frac{1}{3} * 8\frac{1}{4} =$ _____

Write each number in scientific notation.

25. 4,910,000 _____

26. 81,724,691,482,000 _____

27. 862,149,000 _____

28. 33,334,041,100 _____

29. 26,710,400 _____

30. 2,811,462,700 _____

31. 361,247,098,000 _____

32. 320,000,000,000 _____

33. 123,456,789 _____

34. 540,000,017 _____

35. 6,565,656 _____

36. 56,010 _____

Write the number for each of the following.

37. $8^2 + 6^2 =$ _____

38. $10^{10} =$ _____

39. $4^3 + 2^4 =$ _____

40. $7^2 / 7^0 =$ _____

41. $7^2 / 7^1 =$ _____

42. $9^2 + 3^3 =$ _____

43. $2^4 / 2^2 =$ _____

44. $5^3 / 5^1 =$ _____

45. $10^2 * 10^2 =$ _____

46. $11^2 - 3^3 =$ _____

Practice Set 56

Use with or after
Lesson 7·5

Write your answers below or on another piece of paper.

Determine the probability of tossing a coin and achieving the given outcome.

1. heads, heads, heads _____

2. tails, tails, tails _____

3. heads, tails, tails _____

4. tails, heads, tails _____

5. heads, heads, tails _____

6. tails, heads _____

7. tails, tails, heads, heads _____

8. tails, heads, tails, tails, heads _____

9. tails, tails, tails, heads, heads, heads _____

10. heads, heads, heads, heads _____

Solve the pan-balance problems. Assume that each object weighs the same for every pan balance on this page.

11.

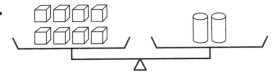

One cylinder weighs as much as _____ blocks.

12.

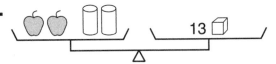

One apple weighs as much as _____ blocks.

Write the greatest common factor for each pair of numbers.

13. 24, 30 _____

14. 12, 48 _____

15. 20, 50 _____

16. 6, 15 _____

17. 18, 25 _____

18. 22, 40 _____

Name _____ Date _____ Time _____

Practice Set 56 *continued*

Use with or after
Lesson 7·5

SRB
110–116
212

Write your answers below or on another piece of paper.

Write each fraction in simplest form.

19. $\frac{4}{2}$ _____   **20.** $\frac{16}{18}$ _____   **21.** $\frac{10}{5}$ _____   **22.** $\frac{12}{24}$ _____   **23.** $\frac{3}{9}$ _____

24. $\frac{2}{20}$ _____   **25.** $\frac{10}{100}$ _____   **26.** $\frac{21}{21}$ _____   **27.** $\frac{18}{20}$ _____   **28.** $\frac{4}{14}$ _____

Find the perimeter and the area of each figure, using the proper formula.

> Area = Length * Width
> Perimeter = 2 * Length + 2 * Width

29.

4 in.

4 in.

_____

30.

7 cm

1 cm

_____

31.

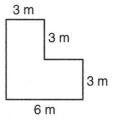

3 m

3 m

3 m

6 m

_____

Solve each problem.

32. Andrea drove 500 miles in 10 hours. Find the average number of miles per hour that Andrea drove.

_____

33. Michael paid $45 for a shirt that was on sale. The original price was $78. How much did he save by buying the shirt on sale?

_____

34. Pat wants to make a double batch of cookies. If the original recipe calls for $\frac{3}{4}$ cup of sugar, how much sugar should she use?

_____

Practice Set 57

Write your answers below or on another piece of paper.

Draw a Venn diagram for each problem. Then answer the questions.

Example   Twelve students in Ms. DeCola's English class read *Sounder.* Eighteen students read a biography of Michael Jordan. There are 24 students in her class. How many students read both books?

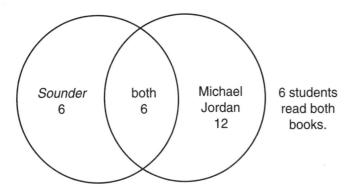

Sounder 6   both 6   Michael Jordan 12   6 students read both books.

1. Twenty students brought all or part of their lunch from home. Fifteen students in Ms. DeCola's class bought all or part of their lunch from the cafeteria. How many students *brought* part of their lunch and *bought* another part of their lunch?

   _____

2. Twenty-two students in Ms. DeCola's class played baseball during the summer. Seventeen students played soccer, and 6 played both baseball and soccer. Twelve students also played tennis. If 4 students played all three sports, 5 students played baseball and tennis, and 2 students played soccer and tennis, how many students only played baseball? _____ only played soccer? _____ only played tennis? _____

Practice Set 57 *continued*

Use with or after
Lesson 7·6

Write your answers below or on another piece of paper.

Match each percent with its equivalent fraction. Write the letter of that fraction.

3. 25% _____   **a.** $\frac{7}{8}$

4. 12.5% _____   **b.** $\frac{1}{2}$

5. 60% _____   **c.** $\frac{9}{12}$

6. 20% _____   **d.** $\frac{1}{40}$

7. 36% _____   **e.** $\frac{15}{60}$

8. 75% _____   **f.** $\frac{9}{25}$

9. 2.5% _____   **g.** $\frac{7}{10}$

10. 70% _____   **h.** $\frac{1}{5}$

11. 50% _____   **i.** $\frac{1}{8}$

12. 87.5% _____   **j.** $\frac{3}{5}$

Find each missing number.

13.

Rule		in □	out △
$\triangle = \square * \frac{1}{2}$		7	
		4	
			3
			18
		20	

14.

Rule		in □	out △
$\triangle = \frac{\square}{6}$		1	
			0
			8
		4	
			2

Practice Set 58

Use with or after
Lesson 7·7

Write your answers below or on another piece of paper.

Tell whether each game is fair. Explain your answer. Each game is for one player and uses number cards for the numbers 1−30, shuffled and placed face down.

1. To win you must draw a number divisible by 5.

_____

2. To win you must draw a number less than 16.

_____

3. To win you must draw a number greater than 30.

_____

4. To win you must draw a number less than 60.

_____

Write the reciprocal for each number.

5. $\frac{1}{4}$ _____ **6.** $\frac{5}{16}$ _____ **7.** 38 _____ **8.** $2\frac{3}{4}$ _____

9. $18\frac{1}{2}$ _____ **10.** $\frac{6}{5}$ _____ **11.** $5\frac{1}{3}$ _____ **12.** $9\frac{1}{6}$ _____

Solve each equation.

13. $3 * t = 21$ **14.** $4 = 60 \div a$ **15.** $x + 6 = (-4)$

16. $14 + s = 42$ **17.** $x * 16 = 64$ **18.** $136 \div r = (-8)$

19. $12 = n \div 9$ **20.** $p - 12 = 2$ **21.** $-2 = g - 12$

22. $19 * v = 133$ **23.** $80 = 21 + s$ **24.** $n \div 11 = 6$

25. $w - 18 = 9$ **26.** $0 = 20 * y$ **27.** $12 + e = 21$

28. $41 - x = 44$ **29.** $52 \div x = 4$ **30.** $v * 14 = (-70)$

Practice Set 58 *continued*

Use with or after
Lesson 7·7

Write your answers below or on another piece of paper.

Write each number in standard notation.

31. four thousand, seven hundred twelve _____

32. six thousand, eight hundred forty-six _____

33. nine thousand, one hundred ninety-six _____

34. one thousand, seven _____

35. 9^2 _____   **36.** 4^2 _____   **37.** 8^3 _____   **38.** 3^4 _____

39. 2^6 _____   **40.** 10^9 _____   **41.** 5^3 _____   **42.** 7^3 _____

43. 6^4 _____   **44.** 3^6 _____   **45.** 12^2 _____   **46.** 20^2 _____

47. 10^{-4} _____   **48.** 10^4 _____   **49.** 10^{-1} _____   **50.** 1.3^2 _____

Find the rule and the missing numbers for each table.

51.

Rule		in	out
		4	8
		10	14
			21
		7	
		0	
			13

52.

Rule		in	out
		21	7
		30	10
			3
			12
		9	
		0	

Find the mean for each group of numbers.

53. 4, 9, 1, 12, 7 _____   **54.** 11, 21, 31, 41, 25 _____

55. 2, 1, 2, 2, 19 _____   **56.** 46, 50, 41, 39, 52 _____

57. 7, 6, 7, 6, 8 _____   **58.** 19, 12, 21, 54, 72 _____

Practice Set 59

Use with or after
Lesson 8·1

SRB
108–112

Write your answers below or on another piece of paper.

Complete the tables and answer the questions.

1. Bacteria grow 2 mm every four hours.

Hours	1	2		4		12	13			
Millimeters			$1\frac{1}{2}$	2	$2\frac{1}{2}$			8	9	$10\frac{1}{2}$

2. If the bacteria kept growing at this rate, how long would they be after 2 days?

(Remember: 24 hours = 1 day) _____

3. Mr. Fikey drove 60 miles in 60 minutes.

Miles				60	71		101	109	120	
Minutes	5	20	45			94				135

4. How many hours would it take Mr. Fikey to drive 660 miles?

(Remember: 1 hour = 60 minutes) _____

5. 16 ounces = 1 pound

Ounces	4			30	38			64	72	
Pounds		$\frac{1}{2}$	$1\frac{1}{2}$			3	$3\frac{3}{4}$			$5\frac{1}{4}$

6. Juanita was making biscuits for a party. She had to quadruple the recipe to make enough. The original recipe called for ten ounces of flour. How many pounds of flour should Juanita buy at the store?

_____

7. It costs $15 to feed 3 guests at John's birthday party.

Guests	1	4			9	12		15	18	
Cost			25	35			70			95

8. John's mother told him that she didn't want to spend more than $125 for John's birthday party. John has 24 students in his class. Will he be able to invite them all?

_____

Practice Set 59 *continued*

Use with or after
Lesson 8·1

Write your answers below or on another piece of paper.

Figure *ABCD* is a parallelogram. Find the measure of each angle.

9. m∠r = _____

10. m∠s = _____

11. m∠t = _____

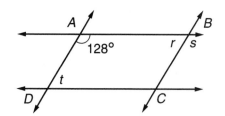

Draw a figure congruent to each given figure.

12.

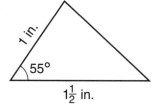

13.

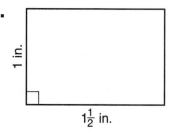

Solve.

14. 1,018
        + 257

15.   18
        * 75

16. 113
        * 28

17. 42)967

18. 18 + 29 + 36 = _____

19. 382 ÷ 7 = _____

20. 489 ÷ 21 = _____

21. 18 * 90 = _____

22. 16 + (3 * 75) = _____

23. 109 − (312 − 286) = _____

24. 239 ÷ 18 = _____

25. 780 ÷ 32 = _____

95

Practice Set 60

Write your answers below or on another piece of paper.

Complete the table and find the missing rule. State the rule in words.

1. Rule: Brad jogs 4 miles per hour.

Time (hr) h	Distance (mi) 4 * h
2	8
3	12
_____	20
_____	40

2. Rule: _____

Time (hr)	Earnings ($)
3	21
5	35
_____	59.5
_____	245

Solve.

3. $\frac{7}{8} + \frac{2}{8} =$ _____

4. $\frac{1}{3} - \frac{1}{3} =$ _____

5. $\frac{2}{4} + \frac{3}{4} =$ _____

6. $\frac{9}{8} - \frac{6}{8} =$ _____

7. $\frac{4}{5} + \frac{9}{5} =$ _____

8. $\frac{9}{7} - \frac{3}{7} =$ _____

9. $\frac{2}{6} + \frac{11}{6} =$ _____

10. $\frac{8}{1} - \frac{7}{1} =$ _____

11. $\frac{2}{2} + \frac{3}{2} =$ _____

12. $\frac{7}{9} - \frac{3}{9} =$ _____

13. $\frac{6}{9} + \frac{1}{9} =$ _____

14. $\frac{8}{9} - \frac{1}{9} =$ _____

Estimate each product.

15. 4.9 * 8.6 _____

16. 4.32 * 8.16 _____

17. 3.60 * 2.19 _____

18. 3.2 * 1.6 _____

19. 7.08 * 6.12 _____

20. 9.28 * 3.10 _____

21. 7.4 * 9.3 _____

22. 1.2 * 3.81 _____

23. 4.82 * 5.34 _____

24. 16.1 * 1.4 _____

25. 2.2 * 3.75 _____

26. 2.16 * 4.81 _____

27. 8.01 * 5.01 _____

28. 6.8 * 1.25 _____

29. 7.51 * 3.26 _____

Practice Set 61

Use with or after
Lesson 8·3

Write your answers below or on another piece of paper.

Solve using cross-products.

1. $\dfrac{3}{5} = \dfrac{x}{10}$

2. $\dfrac{1}{6} = \dfrac{b}{24}$

3. $\dfrac{3}{7} = \dfrac{18}{r}$

4. $\dfrac{2}{3} = \dfrac{n}{36}$

5. $\dfrac{6}{8} = \dfrac{54}{a}$

6. $\dfrac{4}{9} = \dfrac{12}{v}$

7. $\dfrac{6}{13} = \dfrac{c}{52}$

8. $\dfrac{4}{11} = \dfrac{n}{55}$

9. $\dfrac{1}{2} = \dfrac{a}{15}$

Write a proportion for each problem. Then use the proportion to solve the problem.

10. A 40-pound box of apples costs $24. What is the cost of 6 pounds of apples?

_____

11. A case of 12 cans of soup costs $15.48. What is the cost of 2 cans of soup?

_____

12. Mr. Evans drove 376 miles in 8 hours. What was his rate per hour?

_____

13. A recipe for broccoli soup makes 5 servings and uses 3 cups of milk. How many servings of the soup could be made using 33 cups of milk?

_____

Solve.

14. $-20 * 4 =$ _____

15. $-32 \div 8 =$ _____

16. $(-7) * (-9) =$ _____

17. $54 - (-6) =$ _____

18. $-15 + 2 =$ _____

19. $-30 \div 5 =$ _____

20. $49 \div (-7) =$ _____

21. $125 + (-20) =$ _____

22. $-56 - (-18) =$ _____

Practice Set 61 *continued*

Use with or after
Lesson 8·3

Write your answers below or on another piece of paper.

Make name-collection boxes for the numbers below. Try to use parentheses and exponents in each name. Use as many different kinds of numbers and operations as you can. Make at least 7 different names for each number.

23. 42   **24.** 31   **25.** 27   **26.** 13

Solve each problem.

27. Andy works from 7:30 A.M. until 3:30 P.M. every day, 5 days a week. How many hours does Andy work each week?

_____

28. Kelly went shopping and bought a pair of shoes for 20% off. The original price was $49.90. How much did Kelly pay for the shoes?

_____

29. Melinda wanted to bake a cake. The recipe called for 1 pound of chocolate. If Melinda only had 3 ounces of chocolate, how much chocolate does she need to buy?

_____

30. Laura walked a total of 14 blocks on Tuesday. She walked 4 blocks to the grocery store, 5 more blocks to the mall, and 3 blocks to the flower shop. How many blocks is it from the flower shop to Laura's home?

_____

31. Max has $25.00 to spend on a bouquet of flowers. He wants the bouquet to have 4 roses. Roses cost $2.95 each. He also wants carnations in the bouquet. Carnations cost $1.25 each. How many carnations can he put in his bouquet?

_____

Practice Set 62

Write your answers below or on another piece of paper.

Write a proportion for each problem. Then use the proportion to solve the problem.

1. Ms. Lawrence has 36 music students. Two out of every three of her students study piano. How many students study piano?

_____

2. Ruben earns 15 minutes of television time for each 30 minutes he spends on homework. If he spends 4 hours doing homework on the weekend, how much television time does he earn?

_____

3. Complete the following table.

Decimal	Name in Words	Power of 10
0.02	two hundredths	$2 * 10^{-2}$
0.124		
	thirteen millionths	
		$1.08 * 10^{-4}$
	seven thousand, two hundred sixty-eight ten thousandths	
0.00007		
		$5.87 * 10^{-3}$
0.0042		
	two hundred forty-six thousandths	
0.08003		
		$4 * 10^{-4}$

Practice Set 63

Write your answers below or on another piece of paper.

Solve each problem.

1. If 6 puppies are $\frac{3}{4}$ of a litter, how many puppies are in the entire litter?

   _____

2. If 3 kittens are $\frac{3}{7}$ of a litter, how many kittens are in the entire litter?

   _____

3. If 2 eggs are $\frac{1}{2}$ of the eggs laid by a mother bird, how many eggs did the mother bird lay?

   _____

4. If you have read 36 pages or $\frac{1}{8}$ of the total pages in a book, how many pages are in the entire book?

   _____

5. If $3.88 is 12% of the cost of an answering machine, how much does the answering machine cost?

   _____

6. If 12 pounds of aluminum cans account for 40% of the weight of the materials recycled, how much do all the recycled materials weigh?

   _____

7. If 30 students are 15% of the students in the sixth-grade class, how many students are in the sixth-grade class?

   _____

8. If 82 miles are 27% of the miles the Davis family drove in one day, how many miles did they drive in one day?

   _____

Solve.

9. $6.3 * 10^{-5} =$ _____

10. _____ $= 95 * 6^3$

11. $25 * 10^5 =$ _____

12. $1{,}757 * 10^{-4} =$ _____

13. $3.4344 = 34{,}344 * 10^{\boxed{}}$

14. _____ $= 80 * 10^{-6}$

15. _____ $= 3.87 * 10^5$

16. $4.7 * 10^{\boxed{}} = 470{,}000{,}000$

Practice Set 64

Write your answers below or on another piece of paper.

Complete the table.

1. A copy machine was used to quadruple (4x) the size of geometric figures. Complete the table below.

Line Segment	Length of Original Figure	Length of Enlargement	Ratio of Enlargement to Original Figure
Radius	1 inch		
Diameter		8 inches	
Short side of parallelogram		7 inches	
Long side of parallelogram	$3\frac{1}{4}$ inches		
Diagonal of rectangle	$2\frac{5}{8}$ inches		
Base of isosceles triangle		$1\frac{1}{2}$ inches	
Height of isosceles triangle	$\frac{7}{8}$ inch		
Side of regular octagon		10 inches	

Solve.

2. $3x + 4 = 16$

3. $z - 17 = -3$

4. $21 - r = 19$

5. $4 - 3v = 16$

6. $9 + w = 201$

7. $\frac{n}{2} = 13$

8. $2y - 6 = 10$

9. $8c + 2c = 30$

10. $\frac{b}{4} = 7$

11. $4z + 4 = 16$

12. $8x - 2 = 22$

13. $5 + 4a = 13$

Practice Set 64 *continued*

Write your answers below or on another piece of paper.

Solve.

14. $\frac{4}{9} + \frac{8}{7} =$ _____   **15.** $\frac{1}{10} - \frac{4}{42} =$ _____   **16.** $\frac{13}{19} + \frac{5}{5} =$ _____

17. $\frac{7}{9} - \frac{2}{15} =$ _____   **18.** $\frac{6}{14} - \frac{1}{4} =$ _____   **19.** $\frac{2}{5} + \frac{6}{12} =$ _____

Find the perimeter of each figure.

20.

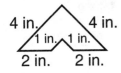

21.

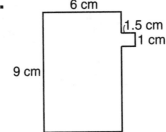

22.

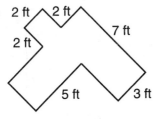

23.

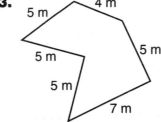

24.

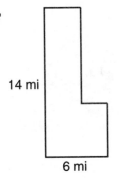

25.

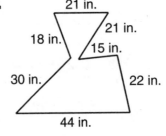

Practice Set 65

**Use with or after
Lesson 8·10**

Write your answers below or on another piece of paper.

Determine the missing measurement for each set of similar figures.

1. $x =$ _____

2. m∠$t =$ _____

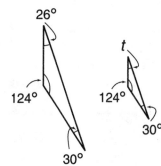

3. $y =$ _____

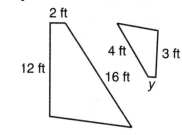

4. $r =$ _____

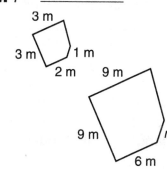

Decide whether each fraction is closest to 0%, 25%, 50%, 75%, or 100%.

5. $\frac{5}{61}$ _____

6. $\frac{12}{13}$ _____

7. $\frac{13}{28}$ _____

8. $\frac{5}{19}$ _____

9. $\frac{89}{96}$ _____

10. $\frac{37}{75}$ _____

11. $\frac{6}{23}$ _____

12. $\frac{45}{58}$ _____

13. $\frac{1}{56}$ _____

14. $\frac{22}{81}$ _____

15. $\frac{56}{73}$ _____

16. $\frac{24}{49}$ _____

103

Practice Set 65 *continued*

Write your answers below or on another piece of paper.

Each statement describes one of the spinners below. Write the letter of the spinner that each statement describes.

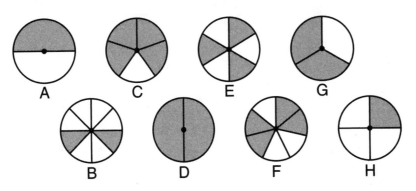

> **Example**   The spinner will land on white $\frac{1}{5}$ of the time. Answer: Spinner C

17. The spinner will land on gray 4 out of 7 times. _____

18. The spinner will always land on gray. _____

19. The spinner will land on white 3 out of 6 times. _____

20. The spinner will land on gray 2 out of 8 times. _____

21. The spinner will land on gray 4 out of 5 times. _____

22. The spinner will land on gray 2 out of 3 times. _____

23. The spinner will land on gray 1 out of 4 times. _____

24. The spinner will never land on white. _____

25. The spinner will land on white 3 out of 4 times. _____

26. The spinner will land on white a little less than half of the time. _____

27. The spinner will land on gray 1 out of 2 times. _____

Practice Set 66

Use with or after Lesson 8·11

SRB
116–119
156 253

Write your answers below or on another piece of paper.

Complete. Give your answer in the hundredths.

1. $\dfrac{35}{15} = \dfrac{}{1}$

2. $\dfrac{57}{84} = \dfrac{}{1}$

3. $\dfrac{101}{59} = \dfrac{}{1}$

4. $\dfrac{74}{50} = \dfrac{}{1}$

5. $\dfrac{720}{990} = \dfrac{}{1}$

6. $\dfrac{250}{300} = \dfrac{}{1}$

7. $\dfrac{830}{670} = \dfrac{}{1}$

8. $\dfrac{456}{300} = \dfrac{}{1}$

Solve.

9. Robbie packed 4 T-shirts, 1 pair of shorts, and 1 pair of jeans. How many different outfits can he make from those clothes?

_____

10. The Mountain Oak Middle School PTA is selling sweatshirts with the school logo. All the sweatshirt styles come in either blue or white. They can be ordered with or without hoods and with or without zippers. How many different sweatshirts can be ordered?

_____

Complete the "What's My Rule?" tables.

11.

Rule

out = in / 30

in	out
180	
	24
630	
	16
4,500	

12.

Rule

in	out
78	−11
99	10
	14
24	
114	25

Practice Set 67

Use with or after
Lesson 8-12

Write your answers below or on another piece of paper.

Find the ratio of the length to the width for each rectangle.

1.

2 cm | A |
3.2 cm

ratio: _____

2. 10 in. | B |
4 ft

ratio: _____

3. 2.5 mi | C |
10 mi

ratio: _____

4.

4 m | D |
4.5 m

ratio: _____

5. Which of the above rectangles most resembles a Golden Rectangle?
Explain your answer.

_____

_____

A driver averages 60 miles per hour. Determine the number of hours needed to reach each destination.

6. Denver: 412 miles _____

7. Hollywood: 180 miles _____

8. Chicago: 68 miles _____

9. Philadelphia: 320 miles _____

10. Orlando: 804 miles _____

11. Phoenix: 72 miles _____

12. New York: 1,091 miles _____

13. Los Angeles: 625 miles _____

Divide.

14. 75.14 ÷ 3.4 = _____

15. 13.23 ÷ 2.1 = _____

16. 15.6 ÷ 0.3 = _____

17. 357 ÷ 4.2 = _____

18. 21.25 ÷ 1.7 = _____

19. 156.4 ÷ 9.2 = _____

Practice Set 67 *continued*

Use with or after
Lesson 8·12

Write your answers below or on another piece of paper.

20. Write the letter for each ordered pair. You will read a mystery message.

___ ___ ___ ___ ___
(−5,7) (10,−2) (2,9) (6,−7) (−4,−5)

___ ___ ___   ___ ___ ___ ___
(7,8) (9,6) (2,−2)   (5,9) (1,−1) (−8,2) (4,6)

___ ___ ___ ___ ___ ___ ___ ___ ___
(7,5) (−8,2) (−6,−6) (8,−6) (6,−7) (5,−10) (−5,2) (−5,7) (10,2)

___ ___   ___ ___ ___
(−8,−2) (8,0)   (2,−8) (1,1) (−7,5)

___ ___ ___ ___ ___ ___ ___ ___ ___
(−1,−1) (7,−1) (−6,1) (6,−7) (−2,7) (−8,−2) (−5,2) (−6,−6) (2,−8) (−7,5)

___ ___ ___ ___ ___
(6,2) (1,−4) (7,8) (−10,6) (9,10)

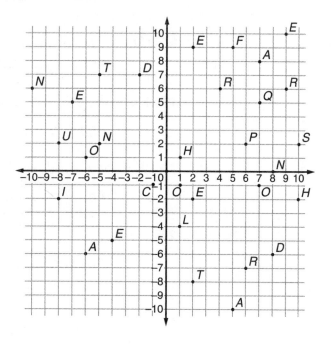

Practice Set 68

Write your answers below or on another piece of paper.

Write the letter of the equivalent expression.

1. $(5 * 17) - (5 * 3)$ _____

2. $3 * (9 + r)$ _____

3. $(17 * 5) + (3 * 5)$ _____

4. $3 * (9 * r)$ _____

5. $5 + (b + 16)$ _____

6. $(b - 16) * 5$ _____

A. $(3 * 9) + (3 * r)$

B. $(17 + 3) * 5$

C. $(3 * 9) * r$

D. $5(17 - 3)$

E. $(b * 5) - (16 * 5)$

F. $(b + 5) + 16$

Divide. Show your work. Write your answers in simplest form.

Example $\frac{5}{9} \div \frac{2}{3}$

$\frac{5}{9} \div \frac{2}{3} = \frac{5}{9} * \frac{3}{2} = \frac{15}{18}$

Answer: $\frac{5}{6}$

7. $\frac{4}{7} \div \frac{6}{11}$

Answer: _____

8. $2\frac{5}{8} \div \frac{1}{4}$

Answer: _____

9. $3\frac{1}{7} \div 1\frac{2}{5}$

Answer: _____

10. $3\frac{2}{7} \div 1\frac{6}{9}$

Answer: _____

11. $6\frac{4}{8} \div 7\frac{1}{2}$

Answer: _____

12. $4\frac{6}{7} \div 5\frac{3}{8}$

Answer: _____

13. $1\frac{1}{10} \div 2\frac{3}{5}$

Answer: _____

14. $6\frac{2}{3} \div 4\frac{1}{7}$

Answer: _____

15. $3\frac{4}{9} \div 5\frac{1}{8}$

Answer: _____

16. $4\frac{1}{2} \div 5$

Answer: _____

17. $7\frac{2}{5} \div 9\frac{1}{10}$

Answer: _____

18. $14\frac{2}{3} \div 8\frac{1}{6}$

Answer: _____

19. $21\frac{2}{13} \div 1\frac{1}{26}$

Answer: _____

20. $10\frac{4}{5} \div 9\frac{19}{20}$

Answer: _____

Practice Set 69

Write your answers below or on another piece of paper.

Simplify each expression by combining like terms.

1. $2x + 15 + 3x - 5$ _____

2. $9t + 5t - 3t$ _____

3. $-3y - 2y - y$ _____

4. $3n - 2 + 2n + 5$ _____

5. $(2\frac{1}{2})y - (\frac{1}{4})y$ _____

6. $7x - 2x + 2 - x$ _____

7. $12x + y - x + 6y$ _____

8. $0.5n + 0.3n - 0.4n$ _____

9. $9h + 4.5 - 7h + 1.75$ _____

10. $3c + 6d - (-7c) + 8d$ _____

Use a Venn Diagram to solve each problem.

11. Kevin's family participates in many sports. He has 8 people in his family. 5 play football, 6 play baseball, and 3 play both. How many of Kevin's family members only play one sport?

_____

12. Jess works at a pool. 47 children are on the swim team. 12 children take diving lessons. 3 children take diving lessons and are on the swim team. How many children are only on the swim team?

_____

13. Chau has a collection of 32 dolls. Each doll has black hair or brown eyes or both black hair and brown eyes. 18 of the dolls have black hair and 20 of the dolls have brown eyes. How many of Chau's dolls have both black hair and brown eyes?

_____

Find the number.

14. 36 is 50% of what number? _____

15. What is 7% of 41? _____

16. 2 is 20% of what number? _____

17. 9 is 12% of what number? _____

109

Practice Set 69 *continued*

Use with or after
Lesson 9·3

SRB
95–96
111–112

Write your answers below or on another piece of paper.

Complete each table. Then find the per unit rates.

18. There are about 2.5 cm in 1 inch.

cm	2.5	5			8.75					
in.	1		2.5	3		4	8	$\frac{1}{2}$	$\frac{3}{5}$	$\frac{4}{5}$

Per inch rate: _____ centimeters per inch

Per centimeter rate: _____ inches per centimeter

19. A cookie recipe calls for $\frac{3}{4}$ cup of sugar for 24 cookies.

Sugar (cups)			$1\frac{1}{2}$			$\frac{15}{16}$		$\frac{9}{16}$		1
Cookies	24	36		60	66		12		6	

Per cookie rate: _____ cups of sugar per cookie

Per cup of sugar rate: _____ cookies per cup of sugar

Add or subtract.

20. (−4) + (−6) = _____

21. 16 + (−14) = _____

22. (−7) − (−51) = _____

23. 27 − (−4) = _____

24. (−13) + (−9) = _____

25. 8 − (−14) = _____

26. (−6) − 5 = _____

27. (−8) − (−3) = _____

28. 13 − (−4) = _____

29. (−4) + (−17) = _____

30. (−8) + 21 = _____

31. (−62) + 10 = _____

32. (−18) − (−14) = _____

33. (−12) − 9 = _____

34. 19 + (−6) = _____

35. 41 + (−21) = _____

36. 14 − (−7) = _____

37. (−8) − (−15) = _____

38. (−26) + 4 = _____

39. 15 + (−2) = _____

40. (−31) + 11 = _____

41. (−112) − 13 = _____

42. (−18) + 3 = _____

43. (−7) − 5 = _____

Practice Set 70

Write your answers below or on another piece of paper.

Simplify each expression by removing parentheses and combining.

1. $2(5 - a) + 5(1 + a)$

2. $r(3 + 7) - 5r$

3. $20(s - t) + 5s + 6t$

4. $3(m + 7) + 18m - 9$

5. $3(8 + t) + (-4t) + 12$

6. $4\frac{s}{7} - 2(\frac{s}{7} + 9)$

Use cross-multiplication to solve.

7. $\frac{4}{9} = \frac{12}{a}$

8. $\frac{18}{53} = \frac{r}{371}$

9. $\frac{5}{8} = \frac{s}{20}$

10. $\frac{57}{70} = \frac{t}{105}$

11. $\frac{18}{54} = \frac{b}{66}$

12. $\frac{9}{72} = \frac{13}{v}$

Solve.

13. $\frac{1}{2}$ of $\frac{1}{3}$

14. $\frac{1}{5}$ of $\frac{2}{7}$

15. $\frac{3}{10}$ of $\frac{2}{3}$

16. $\frac{1}{12}$ of $\frac{3}{8}$

17. $\frac{1}{7}$ of $\frac{1}{2}$

18. $\frac{2}{9}$ of $\frac{9}{25}$

Solve each problem.

19. There are 4 calories in each gram of protein. A piece of chicken has 20 grams of protein. How many protein calories are in the piece of chicken?

_____

20. There are 4 calories in each gram of carbohydrate. If two cookies contain 40 grams of carbohydrate, how many carbohydrate calories do they contain?

_____

21. There are 9 calories in each gram of fat. If there are 144 fat calories in the cookies, how many grams of fat do they contain?

_____

Practice Set 71

Write your answers below or on another piece of paper.

Write the letter of the equivalent equation.

1. $3b + 1 = 22$ _____

2. $\frac{b}{12} + 3 = 1$ _____

3. $7b - 6 = 29$ _____

4. $6b + 10 = 46$ _____

5. $\frac{b}{3} + 7 = 4$ _____

A. $5b - 5 = 20$

B. $2b + 2 = -46$

C. $18 + b = 9$

D. $3(10) - 3(b) = 9$

E. $b * b = 36$

Describe in words the solution set for each inequality.

6. $t > 1$

_____

7. $x < -1$

_____

8. $3d \leq 21$

_____

9. $\frac{d}{4} \geq 20$

_____

Find the measure of each angle.

10. $m\angle a = $ _____

11. $m\angle b = $ _____

12. $m\angle c = $ _____

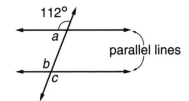

112°

a

b

c

parallel lines

Solve.

13. $17 * (-4) = $ _____

14. $(-11) * 5 = $ _____

15. $(-15) * 4 = $ _____

16. $(-6) * (-8) = $ _____

17. $(-19) * 8 = $ _____

18. $(-16) * 3 = $ _____

19. $(-21) * 12 = $ _____

20. $3 * (-9) = $ _____

21. $(-17) * (-20) = $ _____

Practice Set 72

Write your answers below or on another piece of paper.

Solve each equation. Combine like terms first.

Example	
$7t - 5 = 5t + 3$	
$-5t \qquad -5t$	
$2t - 5 = \qquad + 3$	
$+5 \qquad +5$	
$2t \qquad = \qquad 8$	
$\dfrac{2t}{2} \qquad = \qquad \dfrac{8}{2}$	
$t \qquad = \qquad 4$	

1. $2 + n = 4$

2. $3 * m = 21$

3. $23 = a + 6$

4. $42 = 6 * k$

5. $4 - h = 8 - 2h$

6. $24 - b = b + 14$

7. $x + 3x = 16$

8. $d + 2^2 = 4d - 2$

9. $42 - 3 = 13y$

10. $f + 16 = 5f$

11. $37 + 13j = 27j - 5$

12. $3g - 18 = 6 - 5g$

13. $4s + 3 = 23 - s$

14. $14 - p = 2p - 4$

15. $r + 5 = 3r + 7$

16. $6 + 2q = 10 + q$

17. $8c * 3 = 48$

18. $4t * (3 + 2) = 16 + 4t$

19. $9t - c = 10t + 4c$

20. $6x + 4y = 8y + 3x$

21. $18x + 10 = 20x + 8$

22. $7w + 16y = 10w + 2y$

23. $14a + 6 = 34$

24. $21a - 16 = 0 - 11a$

Practice Set 72 *continued*

Use with or after
Lesson 9·6

Write your answers below or on another piece of paper.

Complete the tree diagram to solve each probability question.

25. 86 people went through this maze. How many people would you expect to end up in Room A?

_____

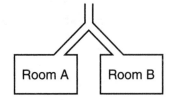

26. 72 people went through this maze. How many people would you expect to end up in Room A?

_____

Room B? _____

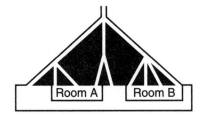

27. 24 people went through this maze. How many people would you expect to end up in Room A?

_____

Room B? _____

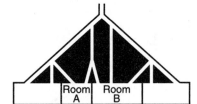

28. 54 people went through this maze. How many people would you expect to end up in Room A?

_____

Room B? _____

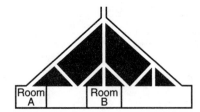

Practice Set 73

Use with or after
Lesson 9·8

SRB
215–218

Write your answers below or on another piece of paper.

Find the area of each figure below.

> Area of a rectangle or square = $b * h$
> Area of a circle = πr^2
> Area of a triangle = $\frac{1}{2} b * h$
> Area of a trapezoid = $(\frac{1}{2} b * h) + (l * w)$

1.

Triangle
7 in.
4 in.

_____

2.

Rectangle   6 ft
18 ft

_____

3.

9 cm   Square
9 cm

_____

4.

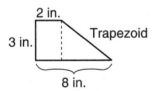
Circle
3 m

_____

5.

2 in.
3 in.   Trapezoid
8 in.

_____

6.

4 cm
3 cm
Triangle

_____

7.

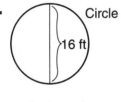
Circle
16 ft

_____

8.

1.5 m   Rectangle
5 m

_____

Practice Set 73 *continued*

Use with or after
Lesson 9·8

Write your answers below or on another piece of paper.

Solve each problem.

9. Martha rode her bicycle 14 blocks to the library. It took her 10 minutes to ride to the library. How long did it take her to bicycle one block?

_____

10. Sara lives 8 blocks from the library. She can walk 3 blocks in 12 minutes. Sara told Martha she would meet her at the library at 3:45. If she leaves her house at 3:15, will she be on time to meet Martha?

_____

11. Jacob meets Martha and Sara at the library. He had rollerbladed to the library. He can rollerblade one block in one minute and 20 seconds. It took him 14 minutes and 40 seconds to get to the library. How many blocks does Jacob live from the library?

_____

12. Manny used a skateboard to get to the library. It took him 6 minutes to skateboard 3 blocks. At that speed, how many blocks could Manny skateboard in one hour?

_____

13. Dan's mother drove him to the library. He lives 3 miles away. On the way to the library, they stopped for 2 red lights that were each 45 seconds long. Dan's mom drove 30 miles per hour. How long did it take Dan to get to the library?

_____

Divide.

14. $43.5 \div 2.9 =$ _____

15. $9.28 \div 3.2 =$ _____

16. $236.6 \div 9.1 =$ _____

17. $16.17 \div 0.7 =$ _____

18. $3.4 \div 6.8 =$ _____

19. $134.4 \div 5.6 =$ _____

Practice Set 74

Use with or after
Lesson 9-9

Write your answers below or on another piece of paper.

Calculate the volume, perimeter, or circumference of each figure.

> Volume of a cylinder $= \pi r^2 h$
> Volume of a rectangular prism $= l * w * h$
> Volume of a sphere $= \frac{4}{3} \pi r^3$
> Circumference $= \pi * d$

1. Volume = _____

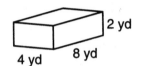

2 yd
4 yd   8 yd

2. Circumference = _____

4.5 in.

3. Volume = _____

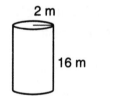

$r = 7$ cm

4. Volume = _____

2 m

16 m

5. Perimeter = _____

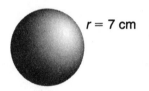

14 in.
6 in.
7 in.
2 in.   2 in.   3 in.
4 in.   5 in.
5 in.
3 in.

6. Volume = _____

7 ft

5 ft   5 ft

7. Circumference = _____

10 cm

8. Volume = _____

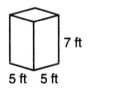

6 m

3 m

117

Practice Set 74 *continued*

Use with or after
Lesson 9·9

Write your answers below or on another piece of paper.

Evaluate each expression.

9. $(-31) + 43$

10. $(-14) - 46$

11. $(-6) * 9$

12. $17 + (-32)$

13. $3 * (-4)$

14. $12 \div (-3)$

15. $(-16) \div (-4)$

16. $(-12) - 54$

17. $(-24) \div 3$

18. $3 - (-4)$

19. $181 + (-68)$

20. $(-14) * (-8)$

21. $12 * (-6)$

22. $(-9) + (-18)$

23. $(-41) - (-3)$

24. $81 \div (-9)$

25. $(-24) * 8$

26. $17 - (-15)$

27. $(-76) \div (-19)$

28. $(-56) \div 8$

29. $(-39) + (-61)$

30. $(-64) \div 8$

31. $(-84) - (-76)$

32. $(-20) * 7$

Make name-collection boxes for the following numbers. Use as many different operations and numbers as possible. Make at least 7 different names for each number.

33. 21

34. 44

35. 77

36. 42.8

37. 25.9

38. 17.5

Multiply. Write each answer in simplest form.

39. $\frac{4}{9} * \frac{7}{6} =$ _____

40. $9\frac{3}{4} * 1\frac{1}{10} =$ _____

41. $\frac{3}{6} * \frac{4}{8} =$ _____

42. $6\frac{2}{5} * 2\frac{3}{6} =$ _____

43. $\frac{1}{4} * \frac{16}{17} =$ _____

44. $7\frac{1}{6} * 4\frac{1}{3} =$ _____

45. $\frac{8}{9} * \frac{3}{16} =$ _____

46. $3\frac{1}{4} * 1\frac{3}{7} =$ _____

47. $\frac{9}{10} * \frac{4}{11} =$ _____

48. $9\frac{6}{10} * 8\frac{1}{2} =$ _____

49. $\frac{2}{7} * \frac{1}{8} =$ _____

50. $4\frac{1}{6} * 3\frac{2}{4} =$ _____

51. $\frac{14}{15} * \frac{8}{7} =$ _____

52. $8\frac{1}{9} * 2\frac{1}{2} =$ _____

53. $\frac{6}{9} * \frac{3}{4} =$ _____

Practice Set 75

Write your answers below or on another piece of paper.

Use the formula to evaluate each situation.

Formula: $3x + 9z$

1. $x = 4$, $z = 7$ **2.** $x = 9$, $z = 3$ **3.** $x = 5$, $z = 0$

Formula: $(c + 4) - b$

4. $c = 2$, $b = 3$ **5.** $c = -3$, $b = 11$ **6.** $c = 4$, $b = 6$

Formula: $t / 4 + s / 12$

7. $t = 8$, $s = 9$ **8.** $t = 3$, $s = -15$ **9.** $t = 0$, $s = 12$

Formula: $f * (g + 2)$

10. $f = 1$, $g = -1$ **11.** $f = 2$, $g = 3$ **12.** $f = 6$, $g = 0$

Determine whether each number sentence is *true* or *false*. If the number sentence is false, correct it to make the number sentence true.

13. $19 + (-7) * 2 = 5$ _____

14. $76 = 8^2 + 3^2$ _____

15. $3 * 12 + 4 = 8 - 6 * -8$ _____

16. $16 \div 2 + 1 = 18 \div 3 + 3$ _____

17. $4 + 9 = 19 - 6$ _____

18. $3^2 + 4^2 = 7^2$ _____

19. $81 \div 9 * 2 = 27 * \frac{2}{3}$ _____

Practice Set 76

Use with or after
Lesson 9-12

Write your answers below or on another piece of paper.

Use the Pythagorean Theorem to determine the missing length of each triangle.
Round your answer to the nearest tenth.

> Pythagorean Theorem
> $$a^2 + b^2 = c^2$$
> where a and b are the legs of the
> triangle and c is the hypotenuse

1.

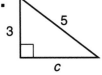

2.

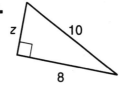

3.

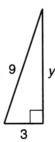

_____   _____   _____

4.

5.

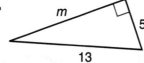

6.

_____   _____   _____

7.

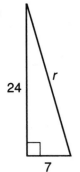

8.

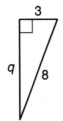

9.

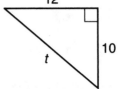

_____   _____   _____

Practice Set 76 *continued*

Write your answers below or on another piece of paper.

Complete each table.

10. Rule: $s = (19 - 4) + 2t$

t	s
−3	
0	
5	
$\frac{1}{2}$	
3	

11. Rule: $z = 4 * (c + 6)$

c	z
6	
9	
4	
0	
−1	

12. Rule: $(18 - p) * \frac{1}{2} = q$

p	q
	6
	1
	3
	0
	2

13. Rule: $7m * (2 + 3) = b$

m	b
	70
	0
	35
	105
	5

Tell if each statement about this spinner is *true* or *false*.

14. The spinner is more likely to land on white than on gray.

_____

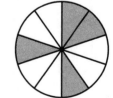

15. The probability of the spinner landing on white is 3 out of 5.

_____

16. The probability of the spinner landing on gray is 6 out of 10.

_____

121

Practice Set 77

SRB
179

Write your answers below or on another piece of paper.

Find the missing measurement for each similar figure.

1. $x =$ _____

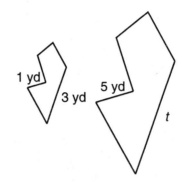

2. $t =$ _____

3. $d =$ _____

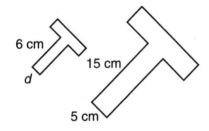

4. $r =$ _____

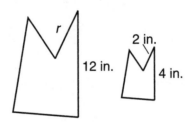

5. $s =$ _____

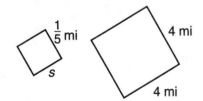

6. $b =$ _____

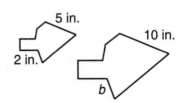

Name _____ Date _____ Time _____

Write your answers below or on another piece of paper.

Ellen made a table to show how she uses her allowance money each week.

How I Use My Weekly Allowance	
Expense	**Amount**
Bus fare	$3.00
Lunches	$6.00
Savings	$1.00
Other	$2.00

7. How much is Ellen's allowance each week?

_____

8. What percent of her allowance does she use for

    a. bus fare? _____

    b. lunches? _____

    c. savings? _____

    d. other? _____

9. Calculate the degree measures for each sector of a circle graph to show how Ellen uses her allowance.

    a. bus fare _____

    b. lunches _____

    c. savings _____

    d. other _____

10. Draw a circle graph showing how Ellen uses her allowance.

Solve each equation.

11. $q + (7 * 3) = 31$

12. $7 * (n \div 8) = 14$

13. $8 = s \div 4 + 3$

14. $92 = r + 11$

15. $4w - 7 = w \div 2$

16. $20 \div w = w * 5$

17. $-12 = (104 \div 2) - t * 4$

18. $(3 * z) + 4 = 0.5 + (z * 5)$

Practice Set 78

Use with or after
Lesson 10-2

SRB
252–253
357–358

Write your answers below or on another piece of paper.

Tell whether each figure would tessellate. Write *yes* or *no*.

1.

_____

2.

_____

3.

_____

4.

_____

5.

_____

6.

_____

Complete the table. Then graph the data. Connect the points.

7. Peanuts cost $1.95 per pound.

Rule: Cost = $1.95 per pound * the number of pounds

Formula: $C = \$1.95 * w$

8. Plot a point to show the cost of 4.5 pounds of peanuts. How much do they cost?

_____

Weight (lb)	Cost ($)
1	$1.95
0.5	
	$3.90
3	
8	

9. Cole, a large dog, can eat 3 cups of dog food per day.

Rule: Amount of food = 3 cups per day * the number of days

Formula: $F = d * 3$

_____

10. Plot a point to show how many cups of food Cole ate in $3\frac{2}{3}$ days. How much did he eat?

_____

Food (cups)	Days
9	
	$2\frac{1}{3}$
	$\frac{2}{3}$
10	
	4

Practice Set 78 *continued*

Use with or after
Lesson 10·2

Write your answers below or on another piece of paper.

Give the coordinates of the ordered pair associated with each letter.

11. H _____   **12.** K _____   **13.** C _____   **14.** A _____

15. D _____   **16.** S _____   **17.** T _____   **18.** G _____

19. Y _____   **20.** V _____   **21.** L _____   **22.** I _____

23. J _____   **24.** B _____   **25.** W _____   **26.** X _____

27. Q _____   **28.** R _____   **29.** M _____   **30.** P _____

31. Z _____   **32.** E _____   **33.** F _____   **34.** N _____

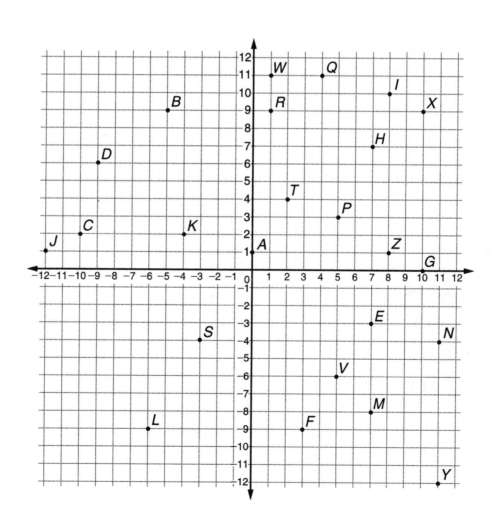

Practice Set 79

Write your answers below or on another piece of paper.

Tell whether each dotted line is a line of symmetry. Write *yes* or *no*.

1.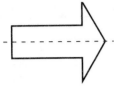

2.

3.

_____   _____   _____

Write and solve an equation for each situation.

4. Cassie had $20. She bought 3 copies of a book for *b* dollars each. She had $2 left. How much did each book cost?

_____

_____

5. On Saturday Brad mowed 3 lawns for *d* dollars each. He spent $5 for lunch. At the end of the day he had $40. Much did he earn mowing each lawn?

_____

_____

Choose the formula that describes the rule. Circle the letter of your choice.

6. a. $2m - 3.192 = n$
b. $m + 1.28 = n$
c. $m * 1.4 = n$

7. a. $v * v = k$
b. $v^3 = k$
c. $5v + 100 = k$

in (*m*)	out (*n*)
3.2	4.48
5.32	7.448
7.6	10.64
10.1	14.14
2	2.8

v	*k*
2	8
3	27
5	125
7	343
8	512

Practice Set 80

Write your answers below or on another piece of paper.

Describe the shape of each cross-section.

1.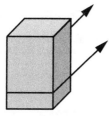

_____

2.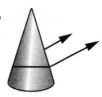

_____

Estimate equivalent percents for each fraction.

3. $\frac{8}{9}$ _____

4. $\frac{29}{99}$ _____

5. $\frac{6}{33}$ _____

6. $\frac{70}{201}$ _____

7. $\frac{2}{23}$ _____

8. $\frac{19}{48}$ _____

9. $\frac{12}{37}$ _____

10. $\frac{7}{11}$ _____

Complete each table. Then find the per unit rates.

11. A tree grows $\frac{1}{2}$ inch in diameter per year.

Inches	$\frac{1}{2}$		$3\frac{1}{2}$			4		$\frac{3}{4}$	$\frac{1}{4}$
Year		2		4	5	9		7	

Per year rate: _____ inches of growth per year

Per inch rate: _____ years per inch of growth

12. A printer can produce 50 pages in 2 minutes.

Pages		150	175		75		200	25	
Minutes	2			5		1			7

Per minute rate: _____ pages printed per minute

Per page rate: _____ minutes per page

Practice Set 80 *continued*

Use with or after
Lesson 10·4

. **Write your answers below or on another piece of paper.**

Use a Venn Diagram to solve each problem.

13. Graham was having a tea party. 14 friends came over to his house. 8 friends wanted only tea, and 5 friends wanted both tea and cookies. How many friends wanted just cookies?

_____

14. Brenda needed volunteers to wash dishes and set tables before the fundraiser dinner. 61 people volunteered. 38 people volunteered to just set the table. 17 people volunteered to wash dishes and set the table. How many people volunteered to just wash dishes?

_____

15. The sixth-grade class at Taylorville has 45 students. 22 students are in the band, and the rest are in the math club. 10 students are in the band only. How many students are in both the math club and band?

_____

Use the distributive property to rewrite each expression. Then simplify.

Example	$7 * (3 + 4)$
	$(7 * 3) + (7 * 4)$
	$21 + 28$
	49

16. $(4 + 2) * 9$

17. $(4 + 1) * 2$

18. $25 * (7 + 10)$

19. $21 * (3 - 1)$

20. $14 * (8 + 5)$

21. $(84 - 6) * \frac{1}{2}$

22. $(91 - 7) * 2$

23. $(8 + 17) * 4$

24. $7 * (30 + 6)$

25. $(17 - 16) * 8$

26. $(7 + 3) * m$

27. $v * (2 + 1)$

28. $d * (f - a)$

29. $b * (a + c)$